BABY BOOMER

GAMES

IDENTIFICATION & VALUE GUIDE

RICK POLIZZI

COLLECTOR BOOKS
A Division of Schroeder Publishing Co., Inc.

Searching for a Publisher?

We are always looking for knowledgeable people considered to be experts within their fields. If you feel that there is a real need for a book on your collectible subject and have a large comprehensive collection, contact COLLECTOR BOOKS.

COVER DESIGN: BETH SUMMERS
BOOK DESIGN: MICHELLE DOWLING
PHOTOGRAPHY: RICK & CARLA POLIZZI

Additional copies of this book may be ordered from:

COLLECTOR BOOKS
P.O. Box 3009
Paducah, KY 42002-3009
or
Rick Polizzi
3400 Greenfield Ave. #7
Los Angeles, CA 90034

@ $24.95. Add $2.00 for postage and handling.

Copyright: Rick Polizzi, 1995

DEDICATED TO:
To my beautiful daughter, Hannah, and wife, Carla.
The only two people who can always make me laugh.

_____

THANKS TO:
Desi Scarpone, Bob Barett, Paul Fink, Eddy Goldfarb,
Dave Holifield, Leon Janzen, R.J. Klimpert, Jeff Lowe,
Kevin Radecker, Fred Schaefer, Alfonzo Smith, Norm Vigue,
Michelle Dowling for her keen design, and Lisa Stroup for
her outstanding care and dedication to this book.

YOU CAN ALSO BUY GAMES FROM:

Paul Fink
P.O. Box 488
Kent, CT 06757
(203) 927-4001

Jeff Lowe
5005 Tamara Ln.
W. Des Moines, IA 50265
(515) 226-9404

INTRODUCTION

When I was nine years old, my parents took my brother, Joey, and me to Disney-land in California. It was the trip of a lifetime. We flew from our home in New Orleans to San Francisco for the cultural portion of our vacation. Then we began the long drive toward Anaheim. Toward Mecca.

After three days and four hundred miles, we pulled into the lot of the Disney-land Hotel at high noon. My brother and I were frothing at the mouth to get to the rides. Forget checking into the hotel! Forget going to the room to freshen up! The park map I had been studying throughout the trip showed there was a restroom right inside the main gate near Great Moments with Mr. Lincoln, we could all "freshen up" there. Instead, what did my parents do? They promptly made reservations in the hotel restaurant for lunch. We were a few feet away from every kids dream and they wanted to EAT! I remember thinking how cruel this was and how I'd never, ever make my kids eat if their Keds were pointed in the direction of the adolescent equivalent of 50 yard line seats to the Super Bowl.

Why the hell are you telling me this story, you're probably asking? Well, to me, long introductions are like that unwanted meal. Talk, talk, talk! Dammit, get me to the rides! So, this will be one of the shortest introductions you'll ever see. Nobody's going to accuse me of being a bad parent. Just a few notes about the prices, the categories... and I'll be out of your way. You can hit every E ticket ride till you turn three shades darker than the Incredible Hulk.

PRICES

The prices in this book, for the most part, are an average of prices <u>paid</u> for games by collectors through surveys by collectors, dealers, dealing collectors, collecting dealers, etc. In addition, prices for some items that aren't seen that often were culled from dealer opinions around the country. Prices from auctions weren't usually factored in because many times they can be over-inflated and not a true barometer of what things are realistically worth. Just because some guy with more money than brains pays a high price for an item he was fanatical about as a kid, doesn't mean the value of that item automatically goes up. If a neophyte pays too much for something, it usually means that he didn't have the patience to shop around.

CONDITION

The prices reflected here are for games in Very Good to Excellent condition. That means a fairly clean, unfaded cover, and all corners and implements intact. If the item is mechanical or battery-operated, it should be in working order. If you have an example in Near Mint to Mint condition, (pieces and cards unpunched, perfect cover) add 20 to 30% to the prices here. If the game is in less than Very Good condition or missing pieces, subtract 30 to 60%. That's right, 60%. I'm tired of going to some collectible stores (actually they're museums, since their pricing definitely tells the customer, "gawk, don't buy") to find I need a co-signer to purchase a common or beat-up game.

TIMELINE

Although a game or two may slip in from other time periods, this book includes games manufactured just after we kicked some Nazi butt in WWII and ends somewhere around our nation's bicentennial. How's that for patriotism?!

DESIGNERS

Many games were designed by in-house Research and Development staffs and therefore not credited to a single person, but wherever possible, the primary designer is listed. Also, when known, the person responsible for box and/or board art is given credit.

This is meant to be a companion piece to the book *Spin Again: Board Games From the Fifties and Sixties* by Rick Polizzi and Fred Schaefer (Chronicle 1991), so the chapters correspond to those in that book, with a few more added in for lagniappe (that's Cajun for "extra.") Anyway, enough of all this chit-chat —

LET THE GAMES BEGIN!

Δ Indicates game is pictured.

DON'T TOUCH THAT DIAL!

If it was on the air in the sixties, chances are there's probably a board game named after it. Game companies went ga-ga over the chance to have their logo emblazoned next to a program that the public was seemingly programmed to tune into. Therefore, the marriage of television and toys was a match made in heaven. It's strange to note that while games were released for such short-lived shows like "Margie" or "Broadside," other classic programs ("I Love Lucy," "The Andy Griffith Show") were overlooked. Maybe after we've solved the mysteries of the pyramids, we can get to work on that enigma. If you don't see one of your favorite shows in this chapter, remember that more TV games can be found in other chapters such as Our Next Contestant Is..., Pajamas And Cereal, No Boys Allowed!, Howdy Pardner!

♟ 77 Sunset Strip $50.00
Lowell, 1960
Designer: Julie Cooper

♟ Archie Bunker's Card Game $15.00
Milton Bradley, 1972
Designer: Bill Burke

♟ All in the Family $15.00
Milton Bradley, 1972
Designer: Bill Burke

♟ Apple's Way $17.00
Milton Bradley, 1974

⅄ Aquanauts $45.00

Transogram, 1961

Transogram had double trouble with this one. Not only did the show last just one season, thus limiting sales, but in mid-season, the producers replaced the star and changed the name of the show to "Malibu Run." Three years later, Transogram re-released this game under a new title — Gangway For Fun, based on the show "Broadside."

Archie Bunker Poker $20.00

Cadeaux, 1972

Game came in a container that resembled one of Archie's cigar boxes.

⅄ "Are You Being Served?" $30.00

Toltoys, 1977

⅄ Arrest and Trial $45.00

Transogram, 1963

Same game as Dragnet and Perry Mason.

As the World Turns $28.00

Parker Brothers, 1966

⅄ Bamboozle, McKeever and the Colonel $25.00

Milton Bradley, 1962

Designer: Jim Houlihan

TV's military school comedy was the basis of this hide and seek game.

BARETTA $16.00
Milton Bradley, 1976
Designer: Jim Houlihan

BARNEY MILLER $15.00
Parker Brothers, 1977

♟ BEN CASEY M.D. $30.00
Transogram, 1961
Transogram tried to infuse some graphic realism into their medical game. For instance, the spinal tap reports are next to the convulsion and brain abscess cards.

♟ BEVERLY HILLBILLIES $40.00
Standard Toykraft, 1963
Standard Toykraft's TV games were known for their minimal covers and insides that had nothing to do with the shows.

♟ BEVERLY HILLBILLIES SET BACK
   CARD GAME $23.00
Milton Bradley, 1963
Designer: Jim Houlihan

♟ BEWITCHED $45.00
Game Gems/T. Cohn, 1965

♟ BEWITCHED STYMIE CARD GAME $27.00
Milton Bradley, 1965
Designer: Jim Houlihan

& BIG TOWN NEWS REPORTING & PRINTING GAME $60.00
Lowell, 1955
Players tried to scoop their rivals in covering front page assignments while actually printing their own headlines with rubber stamp letters on real newspaper.

BIONIC CRISIS $13.00
Parker Brothers, 1975

& BIONIC WOMAN $14.00
Parker Brothers, 1976

& BRADY BUNCH $80.00
Whitman, 1973

BRADY BUNCH CHESS & CHECKERS SET $27.00
Laramie, 1973

BRADY BUNCH DOMINOES $20.00
Laramie, 1973

BRADY BUNCH HEX-A-GAME $25.00
Laramie, 1973

& BROADSIDE, GANGWAY FOR FUN $35.00
Transogram, 1964
Based on the TV show starring Dick Sargent, prior to his becoming the second Darrin Stephens of "Bewitched." It's a re-release of Transogram's Aquanauts game.

& BUCCANEERS $40.00
Transogram, 1957

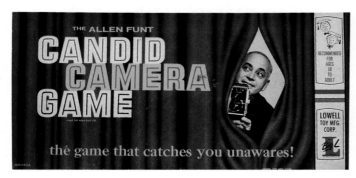

♀ BURKE'S LAW $45.00
Transogram, 1964

♀ BURKE'S LAW TARGET GAME $42.00
Transogram, 1964
*Shoot revolving tires on the escaping criminal's car and
your score would automatically appear.*

C.H.I.P.S. $12.00
Milton Bradley, 1978

♀ CAMP RUNAMUCK $37.00
Ideal, 1965

CAMP RUNAMUCK CARD GAME $25.00
Ideal, 1965

♀ CANDID CAMERA $45.00
Lowell, 1963
Designer: Julie Cooper

♀ CAPTAIN GALLANT $43.00
Transogram, 1955

CAR 54 WHERE ARE YOU? $90.00
Allison, 1962

& Carol Burnett's Card Game — Spoof $30.00
Milton Bradley, 1964
Designer: Jim Houlihan

& Casey Jones $25.00
Saalfield, 1959
Series star, Alan Hale Jr., said of the unsuccessful, syndicated show, "We weren't sure whether we should make Casey for adults or kids. Apparently, it showed."

& Charlie's Angels $20.00
Milton Bradley, 1977
Price is for the Farrah Fawcett cover. The Cheryl Ladd cover is valued at $15.00.

Circus Boy $55.00
Harett-Gilmar, 1956

& Columbo $14.00
Milton Bradley, 1973

& Detectives, The $40.00
Transogram, 1961
Transogram hardly bothered to alter this game when they changed it from Philip Marlowe to The Detectives.

& Dick Van Dyke $75.00
Standard Toykraft, 1964

⚐ DR. KILDARE $25.00
Ideal, 1962
Players moved through Blair General Hospital picking up doctor cards before turning the medical analyzer to decode their patient's illness.

DR. KILDARE'S PERILOUS NIGHT $45.00
Ideal, 1963
In an effort to make some board games more affordable, Ideal created a series of simple games packaged in cardboard envelopes. This one followed the TV doctor on his rounds one stormy night.

DR. WHO $70.00
Denys Fisher, 1975

⚐ DRAGNET $40.00
Transogram, 1955
When Sgt. Joe Friday went into reruns on television in the late sixties, Transogram put this game back in their catalog.

DRAGNET MAZE $50.00
Transogram, 1955

DRAGNET RADAR ACTION GAME $70.00
Knickerbocker, 1955
This game had a rod that steered a magnetic car from underneath the raised board.

DRAGNET TARGET GAME $125.00
Knickerbocker, 1955

⚐ EMERGENCY $10.00
Milton Bradley, 1974

⚐ ENSIGN O'TOOLE – U.S.S. APPLEBY GAME $40.00
Hasbro, 1963

EXPLORING $23.00
Parker Brothers, 1963
NBC released this Saturday morning show in response to the FCC's call for more quality children's programming. CalTec physicist Albert Hibbs took kids on a journey through the world of nature, science, and sociology with the Paul and Mary Ritts Puppets by his side making the trip more fun.

⚐ F TROOP $100.00
Ideal, 1965
Artwork: Ralph Pereida

F TROOP CARD GAME $35.00
Ideal, 1965

FAMILY AFFAIR $50.00
Remco, 1968

FAMILY AFFAIR $40.00
Whitman, 1971

FANTASY ISLAND $13.00
Ideal, 1978
Designer: Julie Cooper

FLIPPER FLIPS $35.00
Mattel, 1965
Players actually flipped small, plastic dolphins onto the

game board to determine their moves. The first one to raise a sunken treasure from the dangerous waters was declared the winner.

FLYING NUN $25.00
Milton Bradley, 1968
Designer: Jim Houlihan

FLYING NUN MARBLE MAZE GAME $55.00
Hasbro, 1967

FUGITIVE $120.00
Ideal, 1964
Artwork: Ralph Pereida
Another version of this game has a small picture of David Jansen on it and is valued at $140.00.

Fury $30.00
Mousley, 1956

General Hospital $17.00
Parker Brothers, 1974

🙎 Gentle Ben Animal Hunt $35.00
Mattel, 1967
Despite the harsh-sounding title, this was actually a very "gentle" game. The winner was the first player to capture and bring home a pet from the Everglades.

Gentle Ben Electric Quiz Game $35.00
Remco, 1967

🙎🙎 "Get Smart" $75.00
Ideal, 1965
Artwork: Ralph Pereida
Once the suction cup time bomb was set, players had to scramble around the board and piece together cards of a master criminal.

Get Smart Mini Board Card Game $33.00
Ideal, 1966

Get Smart "Would You Believe" Game $45.00
Saalfield, 1966

Get Smart "Sorry About That" Game $45.00
Saalfield, 1966

Get Smart Quiz Machine $55.00
Whiting, 1966
This was a battery-operated quiz game that didn't have much to do with the show.

🙎 Gilligan's Island $225.00
Game Gems/T. Cohn, 1965

🙎 Gomer Pyle $50.00
Transogram, 1964
Artwork: Hal Greer
Box showed Sgt. Carter chewing out the "green Marine."

Gracie Allen's Gab Game $45.00
Texall, 1950

🙎 Green Acres $45.00
Standard Toykraft, 1965
CBS's rural comedies such as this, "The Beverly Hillbillies," and "Petticoat Junction," were immensely popular with television viewers until the network closed the barn door on the hayseeds in the early seventies.

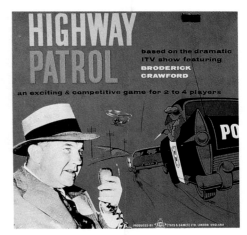

GREEN HORNET PLAYING CARDS $30.00
Ed-U-Cards, 1966

⚗ GREEN HORNET QUICK SWITCH GAME $200.00
Milton Bradley, 1966
Designer: Jim Houlihan
Most Green Hornet items command a relatively high price, and this game is no exception.

GRIZZLY ADAMS $15.00
House Of Games, 1978

GRIZZLY ADAMS $15.00
Waddington, 1978

⚗ HAPPY DAYS $15.00
Parker Brothers, 1976

HARDY BOYS: SECRET OF THUNDER MOUNTAIN $12.00
Parker Brothers, 1978

HAWAII FIVE-O $60.00
Remco, 1968
Remco released a rash of TV games for only a couple of years, thus making them more collectible.

⚗ HAWAIIAN EYE $80.00
Lowell, 1963
Designer: Julie Cooper

⚗ HEE HAW $12.00
Dooley-Fant, 1975

⚗ HIGHWAY PATROL $40.00
Bell, 1959

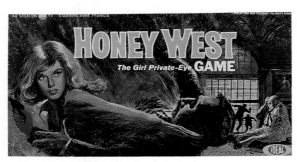

♟ HOGAN'S HEROES BLUFF OUT GAME $80.00
Transogram, 1966

♟ HONEY WEST $70.00
Ideal, 1965
Artwork: Ralph Pereida
Regarding his cover art, artist Pereida exclaimed, "It's the ugliest thing I've ever seen in my life. It's one of my worst!"

♟ I DREAM OF JEANNIE $40.00
Milton Bradley, 1965
Designer: Jim Houlihan
Artwork: Jim Doherty
Following in the wake of network censors, Bradley executives wouldn't allow artist Jim Doherty to draw in Barbara Eden's navel on any part of this game.

♟ I SPY $45.00
Ideal, 1965
Artwork: Ralph Pereida
Game had an ingenious plastic "dueling mechanism" for eliminating counter-spies.

♟ I SPY CARD GAME $35.00
Ideal, 1966
Artwork: Ralph Pereida
This time Culp and Cos take on a sumo wrestler on the cover of the small Ideal box. It's shown here with the original artwork.

♟ I'M GEORGE GOBEL $45.00
Schaper, 1955
Colorful board was full of "Gobel-isms," and the playing pieces were shaped like TV studio cameras.

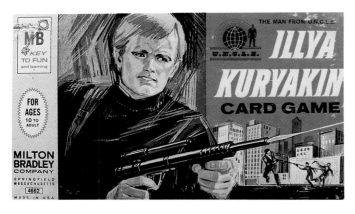

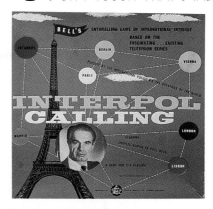

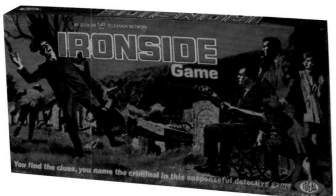

☆ ILLYA KURYAKIN CARD GAME $25.00
Milton Bradley, 1965
Designer: Jim Houlihan

☆ INTERPOL CALLING $40.00
Bell, 1959

☆ IRONSIDE $90.00
Ideal, 1967

☆ IT'S ABOUT TIME $125.00
Ideal, 1965
Artwork: Ralph Pereida
Ideal used the board from its King Zor game in this

game based on the series about two astronauts who found themselves stranded in the Stone Age.

☆ J. FRED MUGGS 'ROUND THE WORLD GAME $120.00
Gabriel, 1955
NBC producers thought that making this lovable chimp a regular on the "Today" show would offset host Dave Garroway's urbane manner. Players of the simian's game got points for collecting actual Pan Am promotional postcards, calendars, coasters, and baggage stickers.

☆ JACKIE GLEASON'S "AND AWA-A-AY WE GO" $90.00
Transogram, 1956

⚭⚭ Land of the Giants — $135.00
Ideal, 1968

Land of the Giants Shoot & Stick — $175.00
Remco, 1968
This large target set came with a rifle that shot "blunt nose missiles."

Lassie — $30.00
Game Gems/T. Cohn, 1965

Lassie, Adventures Of — $45.00
Whiting, 1955

Laugh-In Knock Knock Jokes Game — $35.00
Romart, 1969
This game recreated the famous "joke wall" seen at the end of each show.

⚭ Laugh-In Squeeze Your Bippy Game — $40.00
Hasbro, 1968
One of the most popular shows of the late sixties also inspired one of the ugliest game boxes.

⚭ John Drake Secret Agent — $50.00
Milton Bradley, 1966
Designer: Jim Houlihan
Designer Houlihan thought this was one of his best creations. Unfortunately, it was used on a show that didn't last very long.

Justice — $60.00
Lowell, 1954
You had the chance to solve six thrilling crimes. The game included "the scales of justice" which would actually tip as evidence mounted.

⚭ Kentucky Jones Horse Auction Game — $33.00
Game Gems/T. Cohn, 1965

⚭ Kojak — $18.00
Milton Bradley, 1975
Designer: Bill Burke

☖ Laverne and Shirley $15.00
   Parker Brothers, 1977

☖ Leave it to Beaver Ambush Game $40.00
   Hasbro, 1959

☖ Leave it to Beaver Money Maker $40.00
   Hasbro, 1959

☖ Leave it to Beaver
      Rocket to the Moon $45.00
   Hasbro, 1959

   Little House on the Prairie $15.00
   Parker Brothers, 1978

   Lucan $20.00
   Milton Bradley, 1977

☖ Lucy Show $100.00
   Transogram, 1962

   Major Bowes Amateur Hour $65.00
   Warner, 1954

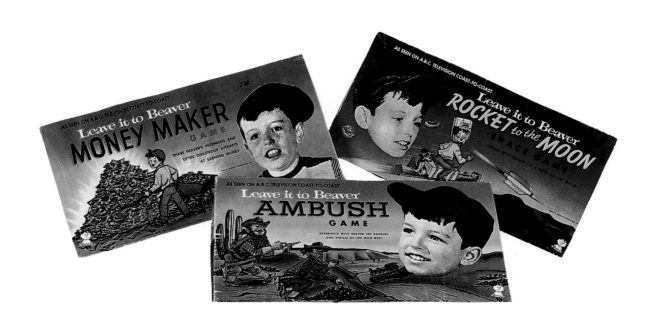

♟ MAN FROM U.N.C.L.E. $35.00
Ideal, 1965
Designer: Julie Cooper
Artwork: Ralph Pereida

♟ MAN FROM U.N.C.L.E. CARD GAME $22.00
Milton Bradley, 1965

MAN FROM U.N.C.L.E. PINBALL AFFAIR $80.00
Marx, 1966

MAN FROM U.N.C.L.E. PLAYING CARDS $35.00
Ed-U-Cards, 1965

MAN FROM U.N.C.L.E. SECRET CODE
    WHEEL PINBALL GAME $325.00
Marx, 1966

♟ MAN FROM U.N.C.L.E. SHOOT OUT! $50.00
Milton Bradley, 1965

MAN FROM U.N.C.L.E. SHOOTING ARCADE $200.00
Marx, 1966
A smaller version valued at $100 was released the same year.

♟ MAN FROM U.N.C.L.E. TARGET GAME $55.00
Ideal, 1965

MAN FROM U.N.C.L.E. TARGET GAME $250.00
Marx, 1966

♟ MAN FROM U.N.C.L.E. THRUSH RAY GUN AFFAIR $95.00
Ideal, 1965
This elaborate game came with a lot of large plastic
pieces that make it more collectible than some of the
other U.N.C.L.E. games.

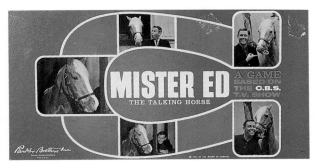

& MR. ED $40.00
Parker Brothers, 1962
Artwork: Lou Green

& MR. NOVAK $43.00
Transogram, 1963

MR. PEEPERS SCHOOL BAG & GAME KIT $50.00
Pressman, 1955

& MARGIE GAME OF WHOOPEE! $20.00
Milton Bradley, 1961
Designer: Jim Houlihan

MARLIN PERKINS' ZOO PARADE $30.00
Cadaco, 1955

& MARY HARTMAN, MARY HARTMAN $22.00
Reiss, 1976

& MCHALE'S NAVY $42.00
Transogram, 1962

MISSION IMPOSSIBLE $70.00
Ideal, 1966
Designer: Julie Cooper
Artwork: Ralph Pereida

MOD SQUAD $65.00
Remco, 1968

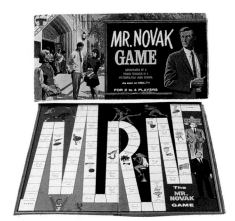

♟ My Favorite Martian $65.00
Transogram, 1963
Artwork: Hal Greer

♟ National Velvet $33.00
Transogram, 1961

Navy Log $65.00
Lowell, 1957

♟ NBC Peacock $15.00
Selchow & Righter, 1967
Players had to collect five puzzle pieces to build an NBC peacock.

♟ NBC-TV News Game with Chet Huntley $42.00
Dadan, 1962
Players tested their knowledge of current events with the dour host of the "NBC Nightly News."

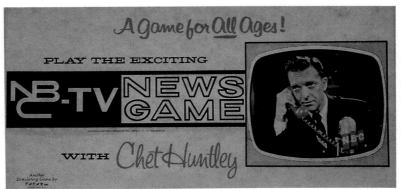

♟ No Time For Sergeants $33.00
Ideal, 1964
Artwork: Ralph Pereida
Like Gomer Pyle, Will Stockdale brought his country ways to military life, this time on an Air Force base. This TV show was based on the 1958 movie starring Andy Griffith.

♟ On The Buses $35.00
Denys Fisher, 1973

Paul Winchell & Jerry Mahoney's
  TV Fun Kit $50.00
Transogram, 1950s

♟ Perry Mason $35.00
Transogram, 1959
Same game as Dragnet and Arrest and Trial.

♟ Peter Gunn $65.00
Lowell, 1960
Designer: Julie Cooper

♟ Petticoat Junction $47.00
Standard Toykraft, 1964
As with most Standard Toykraft items, this game about traveling on the Hooterville Cannonball had lackluster graphics both inside and out.

♟ Phil Silvers, Sgt. Bilko —
  "You'll Never Get Rich" Game $55.00
Gardner, 1955

Philip Marlowe $40.00
Transogram, 1960
This game was re-released one year later as The Detectives.

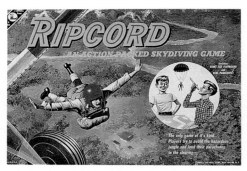

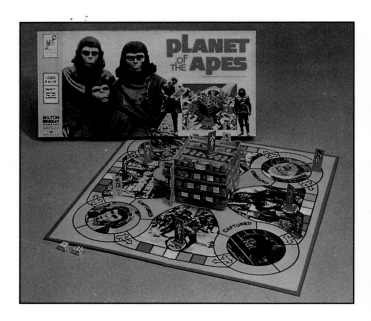

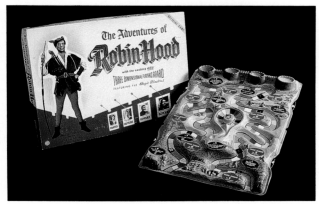

⚑ PLANET OF THE APES $28.00
Milton Bradley, 1974
Designer: Marvin Glass
This game was released during the run of the short-lived TV show, and was sort of a demented version of Mouse Trap. It came with a cage used to capture the human diecut figures.

⚑ RIPCORD $65.00
Lowell, 1962
Designer: Julie Cooper
Object was to blow a parachute up through a tube and try to land in a clearing on the board.

⚑ ROBIN HOOD, ADVENTURES OF $80.00
Bettye B., 1956
Based on the 1955 television series starring Richard Greene, this cool three-dimensional game had a unique "gravity spinner" in which a ball was rolled downhill to determine your move.

⚑ ROUTE 66 $100.00
Transogram, 1962

S.W.A.T. $14.00
Milton Bradley, 1976

SEA HUNT $60.00
Lowell, 1961
Designer: Julie Cooper
As in every other underwater adventure game...find that sunken treasure!

SIR LANCELOT, ADVENTURES OF $65.00
Whiting, 1957

⚑ SIX MILLION DOLLAR MAN $12.00
Parker Brothers, 1975

STARSKY & HUTCH $14.00
Milton Bradley, 1977

♟ STRAIGHTAWAY $38.00

Selchow & Righter, 1961

This was Selchow & Righter's only game based on a television drama. The show's name was changed from "The Racers" to "Straightaway" when the Ford Motor Company became the sponsors and objected to the element of speed that permeated each episode.

♟ SURFSIDE 6 $70.00

Lowell, 1962

Designer: Julie Cooper

Locate the scene of the crime and study fingerprints under your magnifying glass to trap the killer.

♟ T.H.E. CAT $75.00

Ideal, 1966

Artwork: Ralph Pereida

T.H.E. CAT CARD GAME $50.00

Ideal, 1966

Artwork: Ralph Pereida

THAT GIRL $67.00

Remco, 1969

♟ THIS IS YOUR LIFE $45.00

Lowell, 1954

Players moved down "Memory Lane" and advanced through the paths of life until they reached "Success."

♟ TIME TUNNEL $120.00

Ideal, 1966

Artwork: Ralph Pereida

TIME TUNNEL CARD GAME $90.00

Ideal, 1966

Artwork: Ralph Pereida

TIME TUNNEL SPIN TO WIN GAME $95.00

Pressman, 1967

TODAY $40.00
Reco, 1960
A game to test your skill at TV programming. Points were awarded for the strongest programming in each time slot.

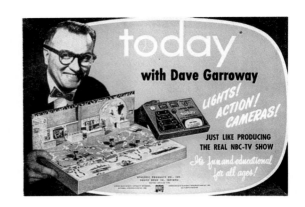

♟♟ TODAY WITH DAVE GARROWAY $130.00
Athletic Products Co., 1950's
This beautiful three-dimensional game unfolded to reveal a miniature television studio.

♟ UNTOUCHABLES, ELIOT NESS AND THE $60.00
Transogram, 1961

UNTOUCHABLES TARGET GAME $175.00
Marx, 1960
Wind-up mechanical target set let you knock down gangsters before they could sell their illegal hootch.

♟ VOYAGE TO THE BOTTOM OF THE SEA $32.00
Milton Bradley, 1964
Designer: Jim Houlihan
Submerge yourself in this game about the super submarine, Seaview, and its struggle to save the world from evil.

♟ VOYAGE TO THE BOTTOM OF
    THE SEA CARD GAME $28.00
Milton Bradley, 1965
Designer: Jim Houlihan

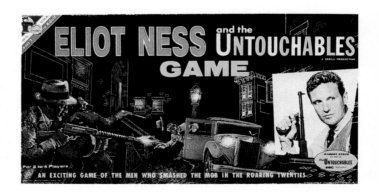

♟ WACKIEST SHIP IN THE ARMY $53.00
   Standard Toykraft, 1965

♟ WALTONS, THE $15.00
   Milton Bradley, 1974

♟ WELCOME BACK KOTTER $18.00
   Ideal, 1976
   Designer: Julie Cooper

♟ WELCOME BACK KOTTER CARD GAME $15.00
   Milton Bradley, 1976

OUR NEXT CONTESTANT IS...

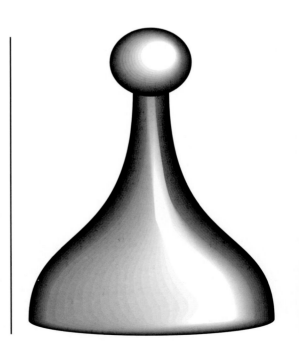

With their roots going back to the early days of radio, game manufacturers liked to publish home versions of game shows because any given title was likely to be familiar to the public. Today, even a failed game show has probably aired five times a week for thirteen weeks and been seen by millions of people. Also, money could be saved in the research and development of these games since puzzles and questions for the home version are recycled from the television version. So you can bet that as long as the shows with the lure of cash and prizes stay on the airwaves, a boxed version will usually be on toy store shelves.

♟ **$10,000 Pyramid** $10.00
Milton Bradley, 1972
Designer: Jim Houlihan

$20,000 Pyramid $10.00
Milton Bradley, 1975
Designer: Jim Houlihan

♟ **$64,000 Question** $40.00
Lowell, 1955
A roulette wheel and slide rule acted as an automatic question selector.

$64,000 Question —
Junior Edition $35.00
Lowell, 1956

$128,000 Question $10.00
Ideal, 1977

♟ **2 for the Money** $30.00
Hasbro, 1955

♟ **Alumni Fun** $20.00
Milton Bradley, 1964
Designer: Jim Houlihan

♟ ART LINKLETTER'S HOUSE PARTY $12.00
Whitman, 1968

♟ ART LINKLETTER'S
    PEOPLE ARE FUNNY GAME $32.00
Whitman, 1954

♟ BEAT THE CLOCK $40.00
Lowell, 1954
Designers: Frank Wayne, Bob Howard
This was Lowell's first game based on a television show.
It included 40 stunts prepared by the writers of the TV
game show. A second version of the game was released
in 1957 with a different cover.

   BEAT THE CLOCK, JR. $35.00
Lowell, 1955
Designers: Irving Kantor, Herb Diamond

♟ BEAT THE CLOCK $14.00
Milton Bradley, 1969
Designer: Doug Beck
Updated version had just as many stunts and also
spawned a second edition.

♟ BIG NUMBERS —
    THE HIGH ROLLERS GAME $16.00
Lowe, 1975

♟ BREAK THE BANK $45.00
Bettye B., 1955
Two editions were released.

♟ BY THE NUMBERS $15.00
Milton Bradley, 1962
Bradley rushed this game into production after the pilot was filmed, but the show by Desilu Productions never made it on the air.

♟ CALL MY BLUFF $17.00
Milton Bradley, 1965

♟ CAMOUFLAGE $16.00
Milton Bradley, 1961
Designer: Jim O'Connor
Contestants hunted for each object camouflaged by a maze of see-through overlays.

COLLEGE BOWL $50.00
Lowell, 1962
Since most game shows did well in the ratings, Lowell was never worried about losing money on one of their home versions.

♟ CONCENTRATION (1ST EDITION) $15.00
Milton Bradley, 1958
Designer: Jim O'Connor
When Parker Brothers couldn't come up with a suitable home version, Milton Bradley bought the rights to this game show to try their hand at it. It turned out to be their first game to sell one million copies in a single year. Over 25 editions followed in the years proceeding. Each of those are valued between $5.00 – $12.00.

♟ DATING GAME $20.00
Hasbro, 1967
Designer: Frank Bresee

DATING GAME PARTY PAK $15.00
ABC, 1967
Designer: Frank Bresee
Contained everything needed to throw a Dating Game party, including invitations and a 45-rpm record of questions.

DIAMONDHEAD GAME $15.00
Gamut Of Games, 1975

♟ DOLLAR A SECOND $40.00
Lowell, 1956
Designer: Julie Cooper
This contained 56 different games, stunts, and outside
events as played on the show hosted by Jan Murray.

♟ DOUBLE EXPOSURE $30.00
Ideal, 1961
Players tried to identify objects and famous personalities
hidden behind a 12-piece jigsaw puzzle.

DOUGH-RE-MI $42.00
Lowell, 1960
This home version came with an eight-key xylophone and a
music book with over one hundred songs.

DOWN YOU GO $22.00
Selchow & Righter, 1954

♟ DREAM HOUSE $15.00
Milton Bradley, 1968

EVERYBODY'S TALKING $18.00
Watkins-Strathmore, 1967

♟ EYE GUESS $10.00
Milton Bradley, 1963
Three other editions were released, all val-
ued at $10.00.

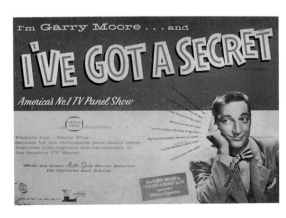

♟ FACE THE FACTS $35.00
Lowell, 1961
Designer: Julie Cooper

♟ FAMILY FEUD $5.00
Milton Bradley, 1977
Eight editions were released. Later editions are valued from $3.00 – $5.00.

FAMILY GAME $27.00
Hasbro, 1967
Designer: Frank Bresee

♟ GET THE MESSAGE $12.00
Milton Bradley, 1964
This tested your knowledge of famous phrases, quotes, places, etc. You had to guess a hidden message from secret, one-word clues given by your team.

♟ GONG SHOW, THE $23.00
American, 1977

GROUCHO'S TV QUIZ GAME $75.00
Pressman, 1954
This was a magnetic question and answer game that was adapted later by Pressman as Ask the Veda Board. It also came with a Groucho make-up kit.

♟ HOLLYWOOD SQUARES $12.00
Ideal, 1974

HOLLYWOOD SQUARES $15.00
Watkins-Strathmore, 1966

♟ I'VE GOT A SECRET $40.00
Lowell, 1956
Designer: Julie Cooper

IT TAKES TWO $12.00
Hasbro, 1969

JACKPOT! $7.00
Milton Bradley, 1974

♟ JAN MURRAY'S CHARGE ACCOUNT $25.00
Lowell, 1961
Designer: Julie Cooper
*Choose letters from the revolving drum and try to
make words in the manner of a crossword puzzle.*

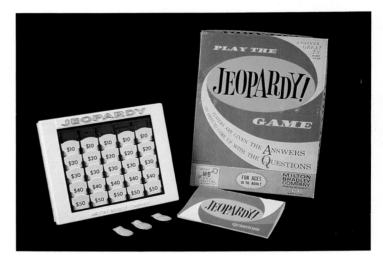

♟ JAN MURRAY'S TREASURE HUNT $25.00
Gardner, 1959

♟ JEOPARDY (1ST EDITION) $14.00
Milton Bradley, 1964
Designer: Jim O'Connor
*Thirteen editions were released and are valued
from $4.00 to $10.00.*

JOKER! JOKER! JOKER! $6.00
Milton Bradley, 1979

JOKER'S WILD $5.00
Milton Bradley, 1973

♟ LET'S MAKE A DEAL $33.00
Milton Bradley, 1964
Designer: Jim Houlihan
*Even though the version Ideal published ten years later is
much more elaborate, Bradley's game is harder to find.*

LET'S MAKE A DEAL $20.00
Ideal, 1974
Designer: Julie Cooper
Artwork: Ralph Pereida

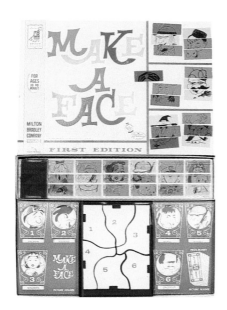

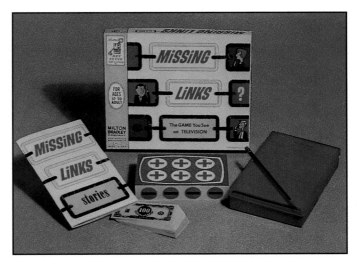

♟ MAKE A FACE $20.00
Milton Bradley, 1962
Designer: Mel Taft

♟ MASQUERADE PARTY $60.00
Bettye B., 1955
This game show had famous guests dress up in dopey costumes and disguises to try to fool the panel.

♟ MATCH GAME (1ST EDITION) $14.00
Milton Bradley, 1963
Eight editions were released. Later editions are worth $4.00 – $8.00.

♟ MISSING LINKS $15.00
Milton Bradley, 1964

♟ NAME THAT TUNE MUSIC BINGO $25.00
Milton Bradley, 1958
Designers: Mel Taft, Jim O'Connor
Milton Bradley combined the success of television's "Name That Tune" with bingo to create this game. It included a record album chock-full of popular tunes. Host George De Witt lent his voice to the record.

NEWLYWED GAME $10.00
Hasbro, 1967
Designer: Frank Bresee
There were three editions produced.

NOW YOU SEE IT $12.00
Milton Bradley, 1975

NUMBER PLEASE $17.00
Parker Brothers, 1961
Artwork: Lou Green

PASSWORD (1ST EDITION) $10.00
Milton Bradley, 1962
Designers: Jim Houlihan, Mel Taft
Twenty-five editions were released, valued from
$2.00 – $8.00.

♟ PDQ: TV Game of Secret Letters $15.00
Milton Bradley, 1965

♟ Personality $20.00
Milton Bradley, 1968

♟ Play Your Hunch $25.00
Transogram, 1961

♟ Price Is Right $30.00
Lowell, 1958
Designer: Julie Cooper

♟ Quiz Kids $30.00
Parker Brothers, 1940

Pay Cards! $8.00
Whitman, 1969

Picture This $27.00
Standard Toykraft, 1963

Price Is Right, The New $17.00
Milton Bradley, 1973
3 editions were available.

Price Is Right: Bid It Right $15.00
Milton Bradley, 1964
Designer: Jim Houlihan
This was a card game based on the The Price Is Right.

♟ Sale of the Century $12.00
Milton Bradley, 1969
Designer: Jim Houlihan
Two editions were released.

♟ SAY WHEN $18.00
Parker Brothers, 1961
Artwork: Lou Green

♟ SEVEN KEYS $23.00
Ideal, 1961
Answer questions on the game board to win the seven keys and all seven prizes.

SKY'S THE LIMIT, THE $40.00
Kohner, 1955
This was based on the show hosted by Gene Rayburn. It followed the popular theme of performing crazy stunts for money.

♟ SNAP JUDGEMENT $10.00
Milton Bradley, 1968

♟ STRIKE IT RICH $40.00
Lowell, 1955
Designer: Julie Cooper

♟ STUMP THE STARS $25.00
Ideal, 1962

SUPERMARKET SWEEP $34.00
Milton Bradley, 1966

& Take It or Leave It	$38.00
Zondine, 1942	
Three on a Match	$10.00
Milton Bradley, 1973	
& Tic-Tac-Dough	$25.00
Transogram, 1956	
Tic-Tac-Dough, Junior	$25.00
Transogram, 1957	
&& To Tell the Truth	$42.00
Lowell, 1957	
Designer: Julie Cooper	

& Truth or Consequences $47.00
Gabriel, 1955
Jack Baily took the reins from producer/host Ralph Edwards when this show moved from CBS to NBC in 1954.

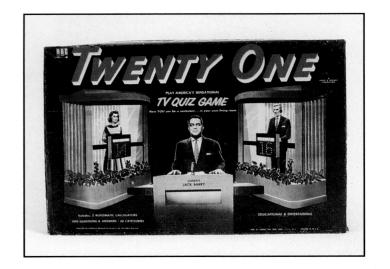

♟ TWENTY-ONE $38.00
Lowell, 1956
Designer: Julie Cooper

♟ UNCLE JIM'S QUESTION BEE $30.00
Kress, 1938

♟ VIDEO VILLAGE $13.00
Milton Bradley, 1960
Designer: Jim O'Connor
Here's the board game version of the television game show that was played like a board game. Contestants were life-sized playing pieces moving down Money Street, Bridge Street, and the Magic Mile.

♟ WHAT'S MY LINE $40.00
Lowell, 1954
As in the long-running television show, players had to guess the occupation of guest contestants (in this case, anonymous black and white photographs) by asking only "yes" or "no" questions.

WHAT'S MY LINE $27.00
Whitman, 1969

WHEEL OF FORTUNE $12.00
Milton Bradley, 1975
Designer: Jim Houlihan

YOU BET YOUR LIFE $65.00
Lowell, 1955
Groucho's game was a race against time as players tried to answer questions, unravel word scrambles, and solve proverbs.

YOU DON'T SAY $10.00
Milton Bradley, 1964
Designer: Jim Houlihan
Players gave their partners three clues by using incomplete sentences. If they guessed three names, your team won money and the chance to play the "Bonus Board."

YOUR FIRST IMPRESSION $30.00
Lowell, 1962

YOUR SURPRISE PACKAGE $26.00
Ideal, 1961
Players contracted for time and raced against the clock to guess the contents of a surprise package. The first player to identify it correctly won the merchandise and all the money they hadn't spent on questioning time.

YOURS FOR A SONG $40.00
Lowell, 1961

WHO, WHAT OR WHERE $10.00
Milton Bradley, 1971
Two editions were released.

WINDOW SHOPPING $38.00
Lowell, 1962

WORD FOR WORD, MERV GRIFFIN'S $18.00
Mattel, 1963
"Contestants" tried to make as many words as they could from letters contained in another word before the Gyro-Timer stopped.

THE SILVER SCREEN

Our smallest chapter contains games based on movies. While the toy industry embraced television, it seemed to treat Hollywood like a pariah. With the exception of a few successful movies, the big screen never really made it to the little board.

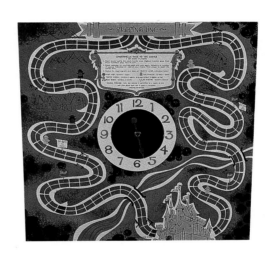

007 UNDERWATER BATTLE $125.00
Tri-Ang, 1965
This large game had the Thunderball poster art on its cover and came with small, plastic frogmen, sharks, and a Spectre submarine.

ALIEN $30.00
Kenner, 1979

ᙰ AROUND THE WORLD IN 80 DAYS $35.00
Transogram, 1957

BEN HUR $45.00
Lowell, 1959
Designer: Julie Cooper

ᙰ CHITTY CHITTY BANG BANG $30.00
Milton Bradley, 1968

CHITTY CHITTY BANG BANG
  ELECTRIC MOVIE QUIZ GAME $75.00
Remco, 1968

CHITTY CHITTY BANG BANG SWITCHEROO $23.00
Whitman, 1968

ᙰᙰ CINDERFELLA $22.00
Dot Records, 1960
Design & Artwork: Ray Gonsalves
The soundtrack album for Jerry Lewis's remake of the classic fairy tale had its own game.

CLOSE ENCOUNTERS OF THE THIRD KIND $15.00
Parker Bros., 1978

⚕ DOCTOR DOLITTLE MARBLE MAZE $40.00
Hasbro, 1967

⚕ DOCTOR DOLITTLE $42.00
Mattel, 1967
Based on the musical which starred Rex Harrison as the eccentric veterinarian who was able to chat with chimps in chimpanzee.

⚕ DOCTOR DOLITTLE CARD GAME $8.00
Post, 1967

⚕ DOCTOR DOLITTLE'S MAGIC ANSWER MACHINE $13.00
Apjac, 1967

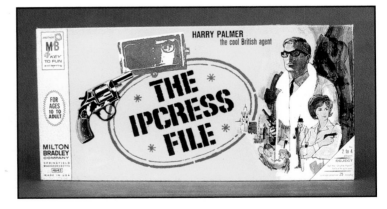

EGG AND I, THE $60.00
Capex, 1947

☋ GAME OF HOLLYWOOD STARS $15.00
Whitman, 1955

GAY PURREE $45.00
UPA, 1962

GODFATHER, THE $35.00
Family Games, 1972
This game came in a box shaped like a violin case. There was
another version in a rectangular box that is valued at $15.00.

☋ GOLDFINGER $35.00
Milton Bradley, 1966
Designer: Jim Houlihan

☋ GOODBYE MR. CHIPS $23.00
Parker Bros., 1969

☋ HOW TO SUCCEED IN BUSINESS WITHOUT
    REALLY TRYING $22.00
Milton Bradley, 1963
Designer: Jim Houlihan
This was based on the hit Broadway play starring
Robert Morse.

I DOOD IT, RED SKELTON'S $60.00
Zondine, 1947

☋ IPCRESS FILE $35.00
Milton Bradley, 1966
Designer: Jim Houlihan

JAMES BOND 007 SECRET SERVICE GAME $30.00
Spears, 1965

JAMES BOND 007,
    ENTER THE DANGEROUS WORLD OF $18.00
Milton Bradley, 1965
Bradley executives must've thought spying and spelling went hand in hand. This was a word game that contained lettered tiles.

♟ JAMES BOND CARD GAME $30.00
Milton Bradley, 1966

♟♟ JAMES BOND MESSAGE FROM "M" $95.00
Ideal, 1965
Designer: Marvin Glass & Assoc.
Game board has scenes of previous movies and plastic pieces of the villains and weapons from them.

JAMES BOND ROAD RACE $700.00
A.C. Gilbert, 1965
Designer: Marvin Glass & Assoc.

♟ JAMES BOND SECRET AGENT 007 $25.00
Milton Bradley, 1964
Designer: Jim Houlihan
A second version of this common game has the same scene on the cover, but 007's face is not Sean Connery's. It's valued at $20.00.

JAMES BOND TAROT GAME $27.00
US Games, 1973
This was a tie-in to *Live and Let Die.*

JAWS $15.00
Ideal, 1975

JONATHAN LIVINGSTON SEAGULL $13.00
Mattel, 1973

KING KONG $15.00
Ideal, 1976

MOVIE MOGULS $10.00
RGI, 1970

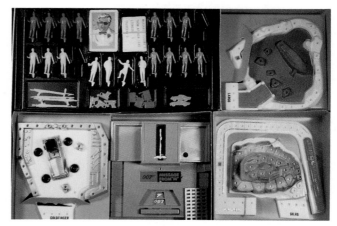

⚉ MY FAIR LADY $30.00
Standard Toykraft, 1962
This was actually based on the hit Broadway play.

⚉ SHOW-BIZ $55.00
Lowell, 1956
Designer: Julie Cooper
"The game as played at the Friar's Club."

SINBAD $30.00
Cadaco, 1978

⚉ SONS OF HERCULES $35.00
Milton Bradley, 1966
Designer: Jim Houlihan

⚉ STAR WARS: ESCAPE FROM THE DEATH STAR $15.00
Kenner, 1977

STING, THE $18.00
Ideal, 1976

⚉ THUNDERBALL $44.00
Milton Bradley, 1965
Designer: Jim Houlihan

⚉ UNIVERSE $25.00
Parker Bros., 1967
Cover had scenes from *2001: A Space Odyssey* on it.

49

TURN OUT THE LIGHTS

Monstermania was one of those cool fads that held the nation in its scaly grip. It all started in 1957 when Universal Studios unearthed a vault full of horror films from the 1930s and 1940s. Universal sold the frightening flicks to television stations nationwide and the monster craze took off faster than you could say Bela Lugosi. Also included in this chapter are fortune telling and Extra Sensory Perception games which were on everybody's mind with the popularity of psychic showmen like The Amazing Kreskin and Uri Geller.

25 GHOSTS $17.00
Lakeside, 1969

☖ ADDAMS FAMILY $80.00
Ideal, 1965
Artwork: Ralph Pereida

☖ ADDAMS FAMILY CARD GAME $32.00
Milton Bradley, 1965
Designer: Jim Houlihan

☖ AMAZING DUNNINGER MIND READING GAME $20.00
Hasbro, 1967
Mentalist Joseph Dunninger had his own TV show in 1955 where he would try to read the minds of celebrities and audience members. After the success of Milton Bradley's Kreskin's ESP, Hasbro decided to bring Dunninger out of retirement. A little more telepathy from the Hasbro marketing people to the customers might have helped sales.

☖ ASK THE VEDA BOARD $25.00
Pressman, 1959

51

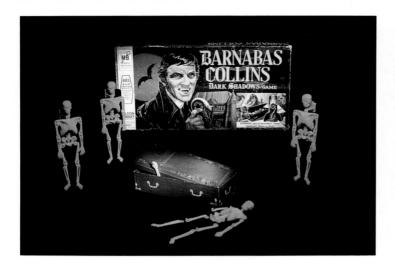

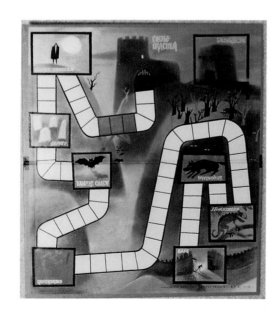

without getting "spiked." A second version of this game had a coffin lid that was cardboard instead of plastic.

Bats In Your Belfry $55.00
Mattel, 1964
Players used a monster claw to catch bats as they flew out of a castle tower.

Bewitch $25.00
Selchow & Righter, 1964
This game of mind reading enabled players to outguess one another.

Boris Karloff Monster Game $130.00
Game Gems/T. Cohn, 1965

Creature Features $20.00
Athol-Research, 1975
This game contained a bunch of black & white cards of classic monsters.

♟ Creature from the Black Lagoon $160.00
Hasbro, 1963

♟ Dark Shadows $42.00
Whitman, 1968

♟ Dracula $140.00
Hasbro, 1963

♟ Barnabas Collins $32.00
Milton Bradley, 1969
Suggested By Harvey-Carlson
Designer: Jim Houlihan
Players retrieved bones out of Barnabas's "beautiful antique coffin" and tried to make a complete skeleton

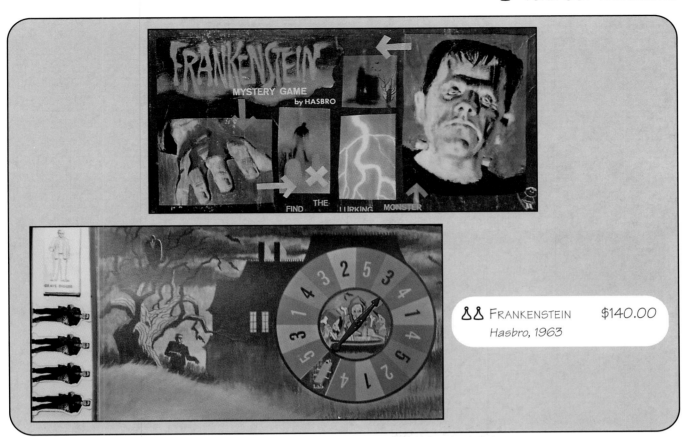

☖☖ FRANKENSTEIN $140.00
Hasbro, 1963

☖ FRANKENSTEIN HORROR TARGET GAME $120.00
Hasbro, 1964

☖ GHOST GUN $50.00
Hasbro, 1974
Gun contained an optical system that allowed you to project and shoot ghost targets on the wall.

☿ GODZILLA $225.00
Ideal, 1963
Artwork: Ralph Pereida

GONG HEE FOT CHOY $15.00
Zondine, 1948
This fortune telling game with an Asian flair is worth it for the name alone!

☿ GREEN GHOST $65.00
Transogram, 1965
Designer: Joe Wetherell
This luminous raised board had three cellars underneath filled with creepy stuff that you had to stick your hand in to find a ghost. By the way the creepy stuff was snakes (rubber bands), feathers, and plastic bones.

☿ HAUNTED HOUSE $215.00
Ideal, 1962
Artwork: Ralph Pereida
Players moved through the house and followed instructions they received behind trap doors and secret passages while trying to find a jewel in the attic.

INTERPRETATION OF DREAMS $15.00
Hasbro, 1969

☿ JEAN DIXON'S GAME OF DESTINY $12.00
Milton Bradley, 1968
Designer: Reuben Klamer

JOURNEY TO THE UNKNOWN $90.00
Remco, 1968

☿ KA-BALA $65.00
Transogram, 1967
Transogram's three-dimensional version of the Ouija board was a mystical trip into the realm of the unknown.

⚱ KING KONG $120.00
Ideal, 1963
Artwork: Ralph Pereida

⚱ KING ZOR GAME $90.00
Ideal, 1962
This game was re-released in 1966 as "It's About Time."

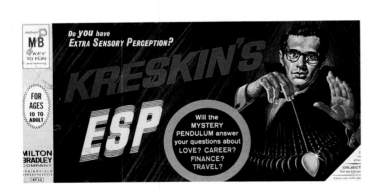

⚱ KRESKIN'S ESP $15.00
Milton Bradley, 1967
Suggested by Kreskin
Designer: Jim Houlihan
Test yourself, family, and friends for that mysterious
sixth sense. A deluxe edition was also released, now
valued at $20.00.

LITTLE CREEPIES MONSTER GAME $10.00
Toy Factory, 1974

MADAME PLANCHETTE HOROSCOPE GAME $11.00
Selchow & Righter, 1967

MIND OVER MATTER $20.00
Ideal, 1967
Designer: Julie Cooper
The Great Julian presented this
game of Extra Sensory Perception.

⚱ MONSTER LAB $230.00
Ideal, 1964
Ideal's original name for this was
Mad Lab. On this three-dimensional
board, set up like a laboratory, players tried to control a masked monster's movement and send him to
their opponent's end. When they suc-
ceeded, the monster would throw up
his arms, growl, and drop his mask
to reveal his hideous face.

 MONSTER OLD MAID $35.00
Milton Bradley, 1964
Designer: Jim Houlihan
A sixties variation of the classic card game.

 MONSTER SQUAD $13.00
Milton Bradley, 1977

 MOSTLY GHOSTLY $15.00
Cadaco, 1975
Cadaco's entry into the horror genre is played exactly
the same as Milton Bradley's Barnabas Collins game.

MUMMY $150.00
Hasbro, 1963

 MUNSTERS CARD GAME $28.00
Milton Bradley, 1964
Designer: Jim Houlihan

MUNSTERS DRAG RACE GAME $140.00
Hasbro, 1965
Box and board showed the Munstermobile in all its glory.

MUNSTERS MASQUERADE GAME $130.00
Hasbro, 1964

 MUNSTERS PICNIC GAME $130.00
Hasbro, 1965

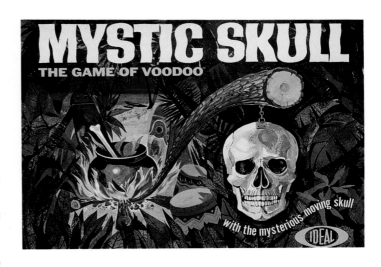

☖ Mystic Eye $30.00
Mr. B., 1953
This fortune telling game asked questions like, "Would you like to go out with Betty Grable?"

☖ Mystic Skull $50.00
Ideal, 1964
The Mystic Skull danced on the end of a gnarled limb and stopped by means of a magnet underneath the board revealing which player's voodoo doll would get stuck with pins.

☖ Ouija $7.00
Parker Bros., 1970s
Designers: Issac and William Fuld

☖ Outer Limits $130.00
Milton Bradley, 1964
Designer: Jim Houlihan

Phantom of the Opera Mystery Game $200.00
Hasbro, 1963

☖ Prediction Rod $12.00
Parker Brothers, 1970
Designer: Reuben Klamer
Klamer (left) demonstrates his mystical game to Parker Brothers president, Ed Parker.

SEANCE: THE VOICE FROM THE
   GREAT BEYOND $30.00
Milton Bradley, 1972
This game had a voice box in the center
that gave you spooky clues and direc-
tions for moving.

☖ TWILIGHT ZONE $140.00
Ideal, 1964
You had to cope with the unknown as
you tried to crash out of the maze on
the board. The first to get back to reali-
ty was the winner.

☖ VOICE OF THE MUMMY $33.00
Milton Bradley, 1971
Suggested By Harvey-Carlson
Designer: Jim Houlihan

☖ VOODOO $38.00
Schaper, 1967
Players took turns putting pins into the
voodoo doll. If the witch doctor sprang
out of his hut, you were out of the game.

☖ WEIRD-OHS GAME $160.00
Ideal, 1963

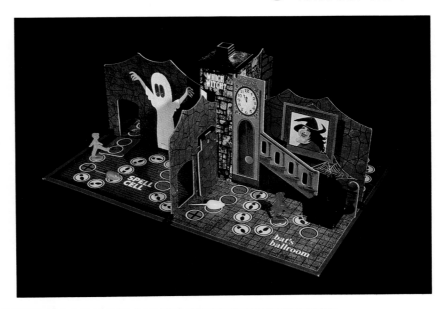

☖ WHICH WITCH $30.00

Milton Bradley, 1970
Designer: Marvin Glass
Travel through the Broom Room, the Witchin' Kitchen, the Spell Cell, and the Bat's Ballroom without being turned into a mouse when the whammy ball fell. This was also re-released in 1984 as The Real Ghostbusters Game.

☖☖ WHY $15.00

Milton Bradley, 1958
Designer: Jim O'Connor
Good Eeeevening — in this game you find yourself locked in a creepy old house with three other detectives, trying to find evidence of why six different ghosts are haunting this place. But first, a word from our sponsor... There were three different covers released for this game. The values are the same for all three.

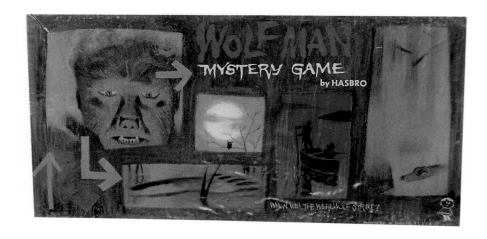

WITCH PITCH $25.00
Parker Brothers, 1970

⚐⚐⚐ WOLFMAN $150.00
Hasbro, 1963

⚐ YIPES $17.00
Ideal, 1976

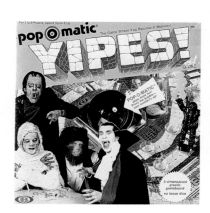

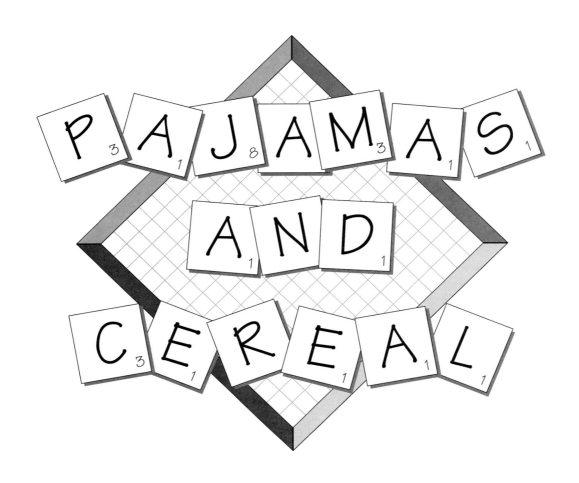

PAJAMAS AND CEREAL

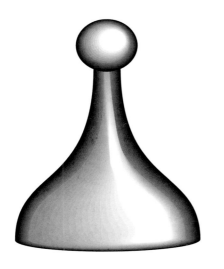

Since the toy industry was aimed primarily at kids, the shows they watched were fertile ground for toy manufacturers. This chapter contains games based on cartoons, children's shows, and comic book characters – the things most cherished by red-blooded American kids.

⚇ ADDAMS FAMILY $35.00
Milton Bradley, 1974
Designer: Jim Houlihan

⚇ AQUAMAN, JUSTICE LEAGUE OF AMERICA $120.00
Hasbro, 1967

⚇ ARCHIE GAME, THE $40.00
Whitman, 1969

ARCHIE'S FUN GAME $50.00
Hasbro, 1963

ARCHIES CARD GAME $28.00
Mattel, 1970

⚇ ATOM ANT $70.00
Transogram, 1966

⚇ BAMM BAMM COLOR ME HAPPY $75.00
Transogram, 1963

BANANA SPLITS $70.00
Hasbro, 1969

☖ BATMAN $45.00
Milton Bradley, 1966
Designer: Bill Burke

☖ BATMAN & ROBIN $73.00
Hasbro, 1966

☖ BATMAN & ROBIN MARBLE MAZE GAME $75.00
Hasbro, 1966

BATMAN BATARANG TOSS $160.00
Pressman, 1966

☖ BATMAN CARD GAME $35.00
Ideal, 1966

BATMAN JIGSAW PUZZLE GAME $44.00
Milton Bradley, 1966
Designer: Reuben Klamer

☖ BATMAN PIN BALL GAME $100.00
Marx, 1966

BATMAN SHOOTING ARCADE $225.00
Marx, 1966

BATMAN SWOOPS DOWN $75.00
Spears, 1960s

BEANY AND CECIL MATCH-IT TILE GAME $22.00
Mattel, 1961
Object was to match tiles containing pictures of the cartoon gang to the edge of the board and each other.

BEANY AND CECIL RING TOSS $40.00
Pressman, 1961

BEANY AND CECIL SKILL BALL $50.00
Pressman, 1961
A wood and metal target was placed on the floor so balls could be rolled into the score areas.

♟ BEETLE BAILEY — THE OLD ARMY GAME $30.00
Milton Bradley, 1963
Designer: Jim Houlihan

BEETLE BAILEY ARMY GAME $45.00
Jaymar, 1956
Game came with small plastic soldiers.

BLONDIE $18.00
Parker Brothers, 1969

BLONDIE & DAGWOOD'S RACE TO THE OFFICE $42.00
Jaymar, 1950

BLONDIE HURRY SCURRY GAME $40.00
Transogram, 1966

BLONDIE SUNDAY FUNNIES GAME $24.00
Ideal, 1972

♟ BOZO IN CIRCUS-LAND $35.00
Lowell, 1965
This character was created by Larry Harmon, who also did the voices of Bozo and his pal Butch.

BOZO POP-OUTS GAME $22.00
Ideal, 1961

BOZO RING TOSS $25.00
Transogram, 1961

BOZO SLING DART GAME $20.00
Transogram, 1961
Suction cup darts came with their own launcher and 12" round masonite target filled with pictures of Bozo and his friends.

♟ BOZO THE CLOWN CIRCUS GAME $30.00
Transogram, 1960s

BOZO TV LOTTO $22.00
Ideal, 1961

BOZO, THE WORLD'S MOST FAMOUS CLOWN $20.00
Parker Brothers, 1962

BREAK-A-PLATE CARNIVAL PITCH GAME — $55.00
Transogram, 1961
Huck, Yogi, and Quick Draw were all featured on small plastic plates that would break apart when hit with the supplied ball.

BUGALOOS — $20.00
Milton Bradley, 1971

BUGS BUNNY — $20.00
Ideal, 1975

☖ BUGS BUNNY ADVENTURE GAME — $38.00
Milton Bradley, 1961
Game included playing pieces with the likenesses of Hanna-Barbera favorites such as Speedy Gonzales, Porky Pig, Pepe Le Pew, and others.

BUGS BUNNY WHAT'S UP DOC? — $20.00
Whitman, 1970

☖ BULLWINKLE AND ROCKY — $50.00
Ideal, 1963

BULLWINKLE CARD GAME — $20.00
Ed-U-Cards, 1962

BULLWINKLE ELECTRONIC QUIZ GAME — $20.00
Laramie, 1971

BULLWINKLE FLI-HI TARGET GAME — $200.00
Parks Plastic, 1961

☖ BULLWINKLE HIDE 'N SEEK GAME — $60.00
Milton Bradley, 1961
Designer: Jim Houlihan

BULLWINKLE MAGNETIC TRAVEL GAME — $40.00
Laramie, 1971
Game was designed like a race course with magnetic playing pieces to keep the kids quiet on those long trips.

BULLWINKLE TARGET AND RING TOSS GAME — $70.00
Parks Plastic, 1961

BULLWINKLE SUPERMARKET GAME — $33.00
Whitman, 1971

BULLWINKLE MOTORIZED TARGET GAME — $150.00
Parks Plastic, 1961

☖ BULLWINKLE TRAVEL ADVENTURE GAME — $40.00
Transogram, 1970

CAN YOU CATCH IT CHARLIE BROWN? $16.00
Ideal, 1976

CAPTAIN ACTION CARD GAME $35.00
Kool Pops, 1967

CAPTAIN AMERICA $20.00
Milton Bradley, 1977

⚲ CAPTAIN AMERICA $60.00
Milton Bradley, 1966

CAPTAIN KANGAROO LET'S BUILD
   A HOUSE GAME $45.00
Gardner, 1956
Included were small plastic tools and various puzzle
pieces to build your own house with the Captain.

CAPTAIN KANGAROO'S PARADE AROUND
   THE TREASURE HOUSE $20.00
Transogram, 1970

CAPTAIN KANGAROO'S TIC TAGAROO $30.00
Milton Bradley, 1956

⚲ CAPTAIN KANGAROO $35.00
Milton Bradley, 1956
Designer: Jim O'Connor

CAPTAIN KANGAROO TV LOTTO $20.00
Ideal, 1961

CAPTAIN KANGAROO/MR. GREEN JEANS $30.00
Fairchild, 1950s

CASPER ELECTRONIC ADVENTURE GAME $85.00
Tarco, 1962

⚲ CASPER THE FRIENDLY GHOST $15.00
Milton Bradley, 1959
Designer: Jim O'Connor

CASPER THE FRIENDLY GHOST $20.00
Milton Bradley, 1959
Designer: Jim O'Connor
This, one of the "Rainy Day Fun" series, was actually
three games in one.

CASPER THE FRIENDLY GHOST $18.00
Schaper, 1974
Designer: Eddy Goldfarb
The best of both worlds for kids who wanted to play in the
dark but were too frightened. This game glowed and lit up.

CASPER'S PICTURE LOTTO $27.00
Built-Rite, 1959
This was bingo with Harvey characters on the cards.

CHARLIE BROWN'S ALL-STAR BASEBALL GAME $38.00
Parker Brothers, 1965

⚲ CHUGGEDY CHUG $38.00
Milton Bradley, 1955

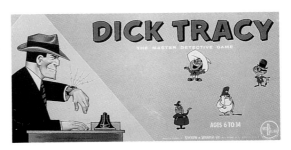

♟ Comic Card Game $25.00
Milton Bradley, 1972

Critter Cards Card Game $25.00
Post, 1965
Pack of cards showed Linus the Lionhearted on the cover.

Crusader Rabbit Game $65.00
Tryne Sales, 1950s

♟ Dastardly and Muttley $30.00
Milton Bradley, 1969
Inspired by the film *Those Magnificent Men and Their Flying Machines*, these World War I aviators were always in pursuit of a carrier pigeon with secret messages for the other side.

Deluxe TV Card Game Set $30.00
Ed-U-Cards, 1961
Box contained Ed-U-Card's games for Huck, Yogi, Quick Draw, and the Flintstones.

Dennis the Menace $75.00
Standard Toykraft, 1960
The winner was the one who could catch Dennis despite his mischievous tricks.

Dennis the Menance Tiddley Winks $30.00
Whitman, 1960

Deputy Dawg $45.00
Milton Bradley, 1960

Deputy Dawg TV Lotto $30.00
Ideal, 1961

Dick Tracy Crimestopper $70.00
Ideal, 1963
This elaborate game for junior super-sleuths had a clue decoder and lit up when the guilty crook's button was pushed.

♟ Dick Tracy Marble Maze $70.00
Hasbro, 1966

♟ Dick Tracy Master Detective $35.00
Selchow & Righter, 1961
Designer: Angelo Longo

Dick Tracy Sunday Funnies Game $55.00
Ideal, 1972

Dick Tracy Target Set $30.00
Laramie, 1969
This set came with two small plastic targets and a plastic gun that shot rubber bands.

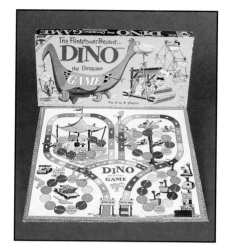

☖ DINO THE DINOSAUR $45.00
Transogram, 1961
Artwork: Harry McChesney
Take Dino on all the rides in the Bedrock Amusement Park
and win the game.

☖ DIVER DAN $50.00
Milton Bradley, 1961
Designer: Jim Houlihan

DONDI FINDERS KEEPERS $30.00
Hasbro, 1960

DONDI POTATO RACE $30.00
Hasbro, 1960

☖ DONDI PRAIRIE RACE $30.00
Hasbro, 1960

DUDLEY DO-RIGHT'S FIND SNIDLEY $15.00
Whitman, 1976

DYNOMUTT: THE DOG WONDER $18.00
Milton Bradley, 1977

ELECTRAWOMAN AND DYNAGIRL $23.00
Ideal, 1977

☖ FANGFACE $20.00
Parker Brothers, 1979

☖ FANTASTIC VOYAGE $25.00
Milton Bradley, 1968
Designer: Jim Houlihan

☖ FAT ALBERT AND THE COSBY KIDS $25.00
Milton Bradley, 1973

♟ FELIX THE CAT $40.00
Milton Bradley, 1960
Designer: Jim O'Connor
This was re-issued in 1968 with a different cover. It's valued at $28.00.

FELIX THE CAT RUMMY CARD GAME $15.00
Built-Rite, 1950s

FELIX THE CAT TARGET GAME $55.00
Lido, 1960

FELIX THE CAT'S DOWN ON THE FARM GAME $38.00
Built-Rite, 1950s

♟ FIREBALL XL5 $90.00
Milton Bradley, 1964
Designer: Jim Houlihan

FIREBALL XL5 MAGNETIC DART GAME $115.00
Magic Wand, 1963

♟ FLASH, JUSTICE LEAGUE OF AMERICA $150.00
Hasbro, 1967

FLINTSTONES $22.00
Milton Bradley, 1971
Designer: Doug Beck

FLINTSTONES BIG GAME HUNT $65.00
Whitman, 1962

FLINTSTONES BRAKE BALL GAME $45.00
Whitman, 1962

FLINTSTONES CUT UP CARD GAME $30.00
Whitman, 1962

♟ FLINTSTONES JUST FOR KICKS $45.00
Transogram, 1962

FLINTSTONES MAGNETIC FISH POND GAME $38.00
Transogram, 1962

FLINTSTONES MECHANICAL SHOOTING
   GALLERY $200.00
Marx, 1962
This domed shooting gallery had a large, plastic dinosaur head as a target.

& Flintstones Mitt-Full $45.00
Whitman, 1962

   Flintstones Pitch 'N Bowl $50.00
Transogram, 1961
8" plastic versions of Fred, Wilma, Barney, Betty, and
their pets Dino and Hoppy were included in this set that
came with balls for bowling or "rocks" for pitching.

   Flintstones Prehistoric Animal Rummy $15.00
Ed-U-Cards, 1961
This price is for the 5½" X 5¼" box. The set that came
as a pack of cards is valued at $8.00.

   Flintstones Sling Dart Game $25.00
Transogram, 1962
Suction cup darts came with their own launcher and an
18" tall figure of Fred holding a target.

   Flintstones Smash-A-Roo Game $40.00
Transogram, 1963

& Flintstones Stoneage Game $35.00
Transogram, 1961

   Flintstones Stoneage Game $55.00
Transogram, 1964
This is the same game as the 1961 version, but only
released for one year.

   Flintstones Stoneage Tiddley Winks $30.00
Transogram, 1962
Kids used "stoneage" hammers to sail their winks into a
target area.

   Flintstones Target Set $75.00
Lido, 1962

   Flintstones Tumble Race $27.00
Transogram, 1961
Two figures on a plastic card would race down a 14" lad-
der. When they got to the bottom, it could be turned
upside down and the race could start all over.

   Flintstones Window Whacker Game $48.00
Transogram, 1962
Vandalism in the streets of Bedrock. This 18" high target of a two-story stoneage building had windows that
would break apart when hit with a ball.

   Funday Cartoons Card Game $20.00
Built-Rite, 1959
Harvey Comic characters were featured on the cards for
this game.

& Funky Phantom $17.00
Milton Bradley, 1971

♟ GEORGE OF THE JUNGLE $75.00
Parker Brothers, 1968
This spoof of Tarzan was created by Jay Ward and Bill
Scott (the voice of Bullwinkle).

GILLIGAN, NEW ADVENTURES OF $20.00
Milton Bradley, 1974
Game included a cardboard build-up of the island.

♟ GOOD OL' CHARLIE BROWN $25.00
Milton Bradley, 1971

GREAT GRAPE APE $15.00
Milton Bradley, 1975

♟ GUMBY AND POKEY PLAYFUL TRAILS $50.00
Co-5, 1968

♟ H.R. PUFNSTUF $30.00
Milton Bradley, 1971

♟ HAIR BEAR BUNCH $15.00
Milton Bradley, 1971

♟ HARDY BOYS GAME $22.00
Milton Bradley, 1970

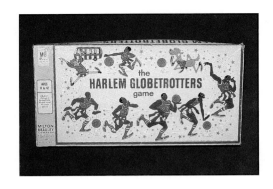

⚱ HARLEM GLOBETROTTERS $30.00
Milton Bradley, 1971

HASHIMOTO-SAN $45.00
Transogram, 1963

HECKLE & JECKLE 3-D TARGET GAME $30.00
TV Film Sales, 1958
This was an embossed plastic target set of the two talking magpies.

⚱ HECTOR HEATHCOTE $80.00
Transogram, 1963

HERMAN AND KATNIP GAME BOX $35.00
Saalfield, 1960
Contained two games, Cheezit and Hide 'n Cheese.

⚱ HIGH SPIRITS WITH CALVIN AND
     THE COLONEL $45.00
Milton Bradley, 1962
Designer: Sid Sackson
Sackson brought his game, High Spirits, to Milton Bradley who liked it, and asked if they could tie it to their new license "Calvin and the Colonel," which was an animated version of "Amos N' Andy."

⚱ HOPPITY HOOPER $75.00
Milton Bradley, 1965

⚱ HOPPY THE HOPPAROO $80.00
Transogram, 1965

⚱ HOUNDCATS $15.00
Milton Bradley, 1973

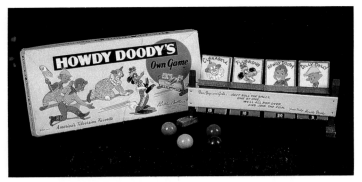

HOWDY DOODY 3 RING CIRCUS $65.00
Harett-Gilmar, 1950

HOWDY DOODY BEANBAG GAME $65.00
Parker Brothers, 1951
The target, which featured a lasso-throwing Howdy riding a jumping horse, had three large holes to toss the beanbags through.

HOWDY DOODY CARD GAME $20.00
Russell, 1949

HOWDY DOODY DOMINOS $60.00
Ed-U-Cards, 1951

☖ HOWDY DOODY ELECTRIC DOODLER GAME $50.00
Harett-Gilmar, 1951

HOWDY DOODY'S ADVENTURE GAME $60.00
Milton Bradley, 1956
Designer: Jim O'Connor
A re-creation of Howdy's TV studio was the setting for this game. It was released three years earlier with a different cover and called "Howdy Doody's TV Game."

☖ HOWDY DOODY'S OWN GAME $75.00
Parker Brothers, 1949

HOWDY DOODY'S T.V. GAME $70.00
Milton Bradley, 1953

☖ HUCK FINN, ADVENTURES OF $30.00
Transogram, 1969

☖ HUCKLE CHUCK $65.00
Transogram, 1961
This three-foot spring actuated replica of Huckleberry Hound let kids attack him from all angles — hook rings on his hat, toss beanbags in his mouth, and throw darts at his target belly.

HUCKLEBERRY HOUND $15.00
Ed-U-Cards, 1961
This price is for the 5½" X 5¼" box. The set that came as a pack of cards is valued at $8.00.

☖ HUCKLEBERRY HOUND "BUMPS" $37.00
Transogram, 1961
Huck and his friends race uphill to see who will be "king of the mountain."

HUCKLEBERRY HOUND JUGGLE ROLL $56.00
Transogram, 1960
Object was to roll a ball down a series of steps and into a cup at the bottom.

HUCKLEBERRY HOUND LIDS OFF
   BOWLING GAME $50.00
Transogram, 1960
Roll the ball and hit plastic figures of Huck to knock off his top hat. Person with the most lids off is the winner.

HUCKLEBERRY HOUND SLITS & SLOTS $22.00
Milton Bradley, 1959
Designer: Jim O'Connor
This was one of Bradley's "Rainy Day Fun" games that played like Tiddley Winks.

HUCKLEBERRY HOUND SPIN-O GAME $42.00
Bardell, 1959

HUCKLEBERRY HOUND TUMBLE RACE $27.00
Transogram, 1961

♟ HUCKLEBERRY HOUND WESTERN GAME $26.00
Milton Bradley, 1959
Designer: Jim O'Connor

INCREDIBLE HULK $10.00
Milton Bradley, 1978

♟ JETSONS FUN PAD $70.00
Milton Bradley, 1963
Designer: Jim Houlihan
Players had to carefully balance "space cars" on the three launch pads without letting any fall off.

JETSONS OUT OF THIS WORLD GAME $100.00
Transogram, 1962
Move the whole Jetson family to your planet before your opponent does.

JOE PALOOKA BOXING GAME $100.00
Lowell, 1952
A three-dimensional boxing ring in the middle of the board had the comic strip character take on five challengers. Players moved their fighters to a decision or a knock-out.

♟ JONNY QUEST $160.00
Transogram, 1964
Every kid wanted to be like Jonny Quest: traveling from one adventure to another with his Dad, Race Bannon, Hadji, and dog Bandit.

JONNY QUEST CARD GAME $40.00
Milton Bradley, 1965
Designer: Jim Houlihan

♟ JUMPING D.J. $28.00
Mattel, 1962
Players pass cards to each other hoping for a match before Beany and Cecil's arch-rival Dishonest John jumps up and ends the round.

৪ KING KONG $33.00
Milton Bradley, 1966

KING LEONARDO AND HIS SUBJECTS $50.00
Milton Bradley, 1960
Game was filled with cards picturing Biggy Rat, Odie
Colognie, Lizard the Wizard, Tooter Turtle, and others.

৪ KORG: 70,000 B.C. $15.00
Milton Bradley, 1974

KUKLA AND OLLIE $35.00
Parker Brothers, 1962
Artwork: Lou Green

৪ LAND OF THE LOST $28.00
Milton Bradley, 1975

LAND OF THE LOST BAGATELLE $25.00
Laramie, 1975

LAUREL AND HARDY MAGNETIC PIE TOSS $30.00
Transogram, 1962
Kids threw magnetic vinyl pies at a large target of the
cartoon duo.

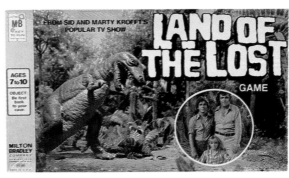

৪ LAUREL AND HARDY $43.00
Transogram, 1962

LAUREL AND HARDY RING TOSS $25.00
Transogram, 1962
Laurel would appear on this 14" masonite target when a
ring hooked Hardy's arm.

LI'L ABNER $30.00
Parker Brothers, 1969

LI'L ABNER'S SPOOF GAME $58.00
Milton Bradley, 1950
Contained small Schmoo cards.

৪ LINUS THE LIONHEARTED UPROARIOUS GAME $80.00
Transogram, 1965

LIPPY THE LION FLIPS GAME $80.00
Transogram, 1962

LITTLE LULU $85.00
Milton Bradley, 1946

⚤ LOONEY TUNES $45.00
Milton Bradley, 1968
Designer: Jim Houlihan

⚤ MANDRAKE THE MAGICIAN $40.00
Transogram, 1966
This game had the magician with the X-ray vision hot on the trail of a set of criminal triplets. It included a set of "magic eyes" to help you with your next move.

LUCY'S TEA PARTY $32.00
Milton Bradley, 1971
Designer: Bill Burke

MAGILLA GORILLA $75.00
Ideal, 1964
Kids helped Magilla return animals to Mr. Peebles Pet Shop.

MAGILLA GORILLA BOWL & TOSS GAME $80.00
Ideal, 1964

MAGILLA GORILLA TARGET BARREL $85.00
Ideal, 1964

MARVEL HEROES CARD GAME $20.00
Milton Bradley, 1979

⚤ MIGHTY COMICS SUPER HERO GAME $150.00
Transogram, 1966
These were characters from MLJ Comics in the 1940s which were revived briefly by Archie Comics.

⚤ MIGHTY HERCULES $125.00
Hasbro, 1963

MIGHTY HEROES ON THE SCENE GAME $90.00
Transogram, 1966

MIGHTY MOUSE $20.00
Milton Bradley, 1958

MIGHTY MOUSE PRESENTS THE GAME OF
    HIDE 'N SEEK $50.00
Transogram, 1962
This was a re-working of the Terrytoons Hide 'N
Seek game released two years earlier.

♟ MIGHTY MOUSE RESCUE GAME $45.00
Harett-Gilmar, 1956

♟ MIGHTY MOUSE SKILL-ROLL GAME $60.00
Pressman, 1959
A wood and metal target was placed on the floor
so balls could be rolled into the score areas.

MIGHTY MOUSE SPIN TARGETS GAME $45.00
Aldon, 1958

MIGHTY MOUSE WITH HIS PALS HECKLE
    AND JECKLE $50.00
Milton Bradley, 1957

♟ MILTON THE MONSTER $33.00
Milton Bradley, 1966

MR. MAGOO $48.00
Standard Toykraft, 1964

MR. MAGOO AT THE CIRCUS TARGET GAME $100.00
    Knickerbocker, 1956
    When you hit the bullseye on this target game,
    Magoo would shoot out of a cannon.

MR. MAGOO VISITS THE ZOO $50.00
    Lowell, 1961
    Designer: Julie Cooper

♟ MR. MAGOO'S MADDENING
    MISADVENTURES $25.00
    Transogram, 1970

Mushmouse & Punkin Puss *Ideal, 1964*	$90.00	

⅄ Pebbles Flintstone — $45.00
Transogram, 1962
Is Dino getting ready to change Pebbles' diaper or is he eyeing her up for dinner? Whatever the cover illustration implies, the game is about the Bedrock phone system.

Mushmouse & Punkin Puss Feudin'
  Hillbillies Target Game — $120.00
Ideal, 1964

Pebbles Flintstone Magnetic Fish
  Pond Game — $55.00
Transogram, 1963

Nancy and Sluggo — $75.00
Milton Bradley, 1944

⅄ Off to See the Wizard — $20.00
Milton Bradley, 1968

Peter Potamus — $180.00
Ideal, 1964

Oh Magoo, You've Done It Again — $20.00
Warren, 1973

Peter Potamus and Yo-Yo Card Game — $20.00
Whitman, 1965

Olive Oyl — I'll Catch My Popeye Game — $45.00
Hasbro, 1965

Peter Potamus Target Barrel — $80.00
Ideal, 1964

Ozark Ike's 3 Game Set — $50.00
Built-Rite, 1956

Phantom's 3 Game Set — $70.00
Built-Rite, 1957

Peanuts — $38.00
Selchow & Righter, 1959
Artwork: Charles Schultz
This game came with a reversible board, one side for adults, the other for kids.

⅄ Phantom, Ruler of the Jungle — $135.00
Transogram, 1965

⅄ Pink Panther — $25.00
Milton Bradley, 1970
Designer: Reuben Klamer

PINK PANTHER $22.00
Warren, 1977

PINKY LEE "WHO AM I?" GAME $50.00
Ed-U-Cards, 1954

♟ PINKY LEE & THE RUNAWAY FRANKFURTERS $65.00
Whiting, 1954

PINKY LEE GAME TIME $35.00
Pressman, 1955
Hey kids, can you "Pin The Tie On Pinky?" This set contained all sorts of party games and favors for the perfect birthday bash.

PINOCCHIO, NEW ADVENTURES OF $40.00
Lowell, 1960
Designer: Julie Cooper

POPEYE 3 GAME SET $50.00
Built-Rite, 1956

POPEYE AND HIS PALS $37.00
Ideal, 1963

POPEYE BALL TOSS $60.00
Transogram, 1966

♟ POPEYE CARD GAME $12.00
Ed-U-Cards, 1961
This price is for the 5½" X 5¼" box. The set that came as a pack of cards is valued at $5.00.

POPEYE CARNIVAL $85.00
Toymasters, 1960
This big game measured 2 feet wide and 5 feet tall and contained a shooting range as well as ring and ball toss games.

POPEYE MAGNETIC FISHING GAME $32.00
Transogram, 1958

POPEYE RING TOSS $34.00
Transogram, 1961
Here was a 14" stand-up masonite cut-out of Popeye. Swee' Pea would appear when rings would hook on the sailor's target arm. A smaller version without the moving arms was also available. It's valued at $15.00.

POPEYE SKOOZ-IT GAME $60.00
Ideal, 1963
Designer: Reuben Klamer

POPEYE SLIDING BOARDS & LADDERS $50.00
Built-Rite, 1958

POPEYE SLING DART GAME $25.00
Transogram, 1961
Suction cup darts came with their own launcher and a 12" round masonite target filled with pictures of Popeye and his friends.

POPEYE'S TREASURE MAP $10.00
Whitman, 1977

♟ POPEYE, ADVENTURES OF $65.00
Transogram, 1957
Players won by eating the right number of cans of spinach, which are won in the "Grand Spinach Lottery."

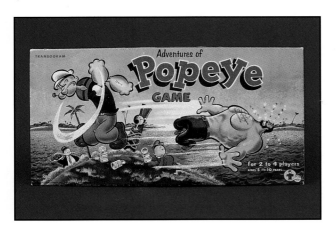

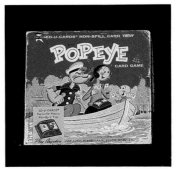

⚱ PRINCE VALIANT $45.00
Transogram, 1955
Artwork: Harold Foster
Although the artwork is taken from the comic strip, this game was actually a tie-in with the 20th Century Fox movie starring James Mason.

PRINCE VALIANT CROSSBOW PISTOL GAME $75.00
Parva Products, 1948
Contained a spring-loaded crossbow with rubber-tipped arrows.

QUICK DRAW McGRAW CARD GAME $16.00
Ed-U-Cards, 1961
This price is for the 5½" X 5¼" box. The set that came as a pack of cards is valued at $8.00.

⚱ QUICK DRAW McGRAW PRIVATE EYE $28.00
Milton Bradley, 1961
Quick Draw and his friends are on the heels of a mystery in this game for junior super-sleuths. Daws Butler did the voices for most of the characters in this cartoon series.

RAMAR OF THE JUNGLE $75.00
Dexter Wayne, 1953

RAMAR OF THE JUNGLE BLOW GUN
   TARGET GAME $75.00
Gabriel, 1955
Cardboard target game came with a blow gun and rubber pellets to fight off jungle nasties.

⚱ REX MORGAN M.D. $23.00
Ideal, 1972
One of Ideal's "Sunday Funnies" games which were based on comic strip characters.

RICOCHET RABBIT & DROOP-A-LONG
   COYOTE GAME $120.00
Ideal, 1965

⚱ ROAD RUNNER $27.00
Milton Bradley, 1968

ROAD RUNNER, GET THE $22.00
Whitman, 1969

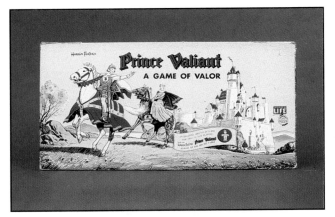

ROCKY AND BULLWINKLE MAGIC DOT GAME $50.00
Whitman, 1962

ROCKY AND HIS FRIENDS $60.00
Milton Bradley, 1960
Designer: Jim Houlihan

ROOTIE KAZOOTIE WORD GAME $15.00
Ed-U-Cards, 1953

ROSEY THE ROBOT $85.00
Transogram, 1962

☖ RUFF AND REDDY AT THE CIRCUS $40.00
Transogram, 1962
Ruff and Reddy were the first TV characters created by Hannah-Barbera. Here, they perform a high-wire act at the circus.

RUFF & REDDY TV FAVORITE SPELLING GAME $28.00
Exclusive Playing Card Co., 1959

☖ SCOOBY DOO...WHERE ARE YOU? $22.00
Milton Bradley, 1973
Designer: Doug Beck

SEALAB 2020 $22.00
Milton Bradley, 1973

SHARI LEWIS IN SHARILAND $50.00
Transogram, 1959
Lamb Chop, Charlie Horse, and Hush Puppy were all on hand in this game for youngsters.

SHARI LEWIS PARTY GAMES $35.00
Lowell, 1962
Came complete with a phonograph record and props for ten party games.

SHAZAM! CAPTAIN MARVEL'S OWN GAME $23.00
Reed, 1940s

SHAZAM! CARD GAME $10.00
Russ, 1977

☖ SHENANIGANS $28.00
Milton Bradley, 1964
Designer: Jim O'Connor
Milton Bradley created this kiddie game show to advertise all of their new products. Another version of this game has a different cover and the Video Village dice-filled hourglass to determine moves instead of a spinner.

SIGMUND AND THE SEA MONSTER $25.00
Milton Bradley, 1975

☖ SILLY SIDNEY $40.00
Transogram, 1963

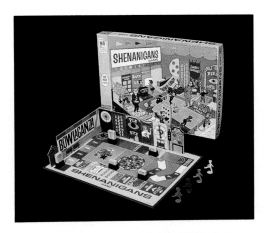

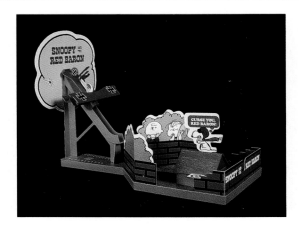

SILLY SIDNEY COCONUT SHOOT TARGET GAME $100.00
Transogram, 1963
The plastic gun was molded in the shape of Sidney the elephant.

SNAGGLEPUSS $40.00
Transogram, 1961

SNOOPY $45.00
Selchow & Righter, 1960
Chase all four of your dogs into their doghouses without Snoopy following behind.

SNOOPY AND THE RED BARON $30.00
Milton Bradley, 1970
Designer: Marvin Glass & Assoc.
Flying high in his Sopwith Camel, the Red Baron pelts Snoopy with colored marbles as the Peanuts gang observes.

SNOOPY CARD GAME $17.00
Milton Bradley, 1968

SNOOPY COME HOME $24.00
Milton Bradley, 1973

SNOOPY'S DOGHOUSE GAME $20.00
Milton Bradley, 1977
Designer: Marvin Glass & Assoc.

SNUFFY SMITH TIME'S A WASTIN' GAME $32.00
Milton Bradley, 1963
Designer: Jim O'Connor

SNUFFY SMITH'S HOOTIN HOLLER BUG DERBY $34.00
Jaymar, 1950s

SOUPY SALES MINI-BOARD CARD GAME $35.00
Ideal, 1965

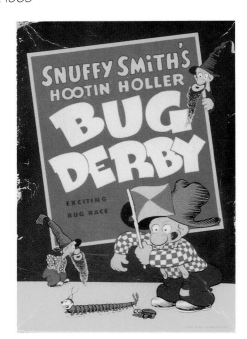

☖ SOUPY SALES $80.00
Ideal, 1965

☖ SOUPY SALES SEZ GO-GO-GO $60.00
Milton Bradley, 1961
Designer: Mel Taft

SPACE ANGEL $85.00
Transogram, 1965

SPACE MOUSE CARD GAME $13.00
Fairchild, 1964

☖ SPEED BUGGY $20.00
Milton Bradley, 1973

☖ SPIDER-MAN $48.00
Milton Bradley, 1967

SPIDER-MAN WITH THE FANTASTIC FOUR $15.00
Milton Bradley, 1977

☖ SPOOKY MARBLE MAZE GAME $37.00
Built-Rite, 1971

♟ Steve Canyon $60.00
Lowell, 1959
Designer: Julie Cooper
Artwork: Milt Caniff
Game contained cockpit control panels for four "pilots."

♟ Stingray $150.00
Transogram, 1966

Stingray Target Game $150.00
Transogram, 1966
This dart gun set had the artwork from the board game on its target.

Super Heroes Bingo $35.00
Hasbro, 1976

♟ Superboy $100.00
Hasbro, 1965

Supercar Road Race Game $75.00
Standard Toykraft, 1962

Supercar Target Game $230.00
Magic Wand, 1962

♟ Supercar To The Rescue $80.00
Milton Bradley, 1962
Designer: Jim Houlihan

Superheroes Card Game $15.00
Milton Bradley, 1978

Superman	$55.00	Superman Spin to Win Game	$60.00
Merry Manuf., 1966		*Pressman, 1967*	
♟ Superman and Superboy	$63.00	Superman's Deadliest Enemy	$40.00
Milton Bradley, 1967		*Hasbro, 1965*	
♟ Superman Card Game	$44.00		
Ideal, 1966			
Artwork: Murphy Anderson			

Superman Flying Bingo $35.00
Whitman, 1966
Designer: Reuben Klamer

Superman Horseshoe Set $80.00
Super Swim Inc., 1950s

Superman Junior Quoit Set $60.00
Super Swim Inc., 1950s

Superman Marble Maze $75.00
Hasbro, 1966

♟ Superman Quoit & Horseshoe Set	$100.00	Superman, Adventures of	$200.00
Super Swim Inc., 1950s		*Milton Bradley, 1942*	
Superman Speed Game	$150.00	♟ Superman, Calling	$90.00
Milton Bradley, 1940		*Transogram, 1954*	

♟ TALK TO CECIL $70.00
Mattel, 1961
Pull Cecil's string and he gives you clues for your next move along the Cecil-shaped puzzle track.

TARZAN TO THE RESCUE $17.00
Milton Bradley, 1977
Designer: Eddy Goldfarb

♟ TENNESEE TUXEDO $135.00
Transogram, 1963
Tennessee, Chumley, and Professor Phineas J. Whoopie are in hot pursuit of some mice that have been scaring the zoo animals. Don Adams, Bradley Bolk, and F Troop's Larry Storch were their respective voices.

TERRY AND THE PIRATES $30.00
Ideal, 1972
This was another of Ideal's "Sunday Funnies Game."

♟ TERRYTOONS HIDE & SEEK GAME $60.00
Transogram, 1960

This was re-released in 1962 with a new cover and re-titled "Mighty Mouse presents the Game of Hide N' Seek."

TERRYTOONS OLD MAID $15.00
Ed-U-Cards, 1960

TERRYTOONS POP-OUTS GAME $25.00
Ideal, 1961

TERRYTOONS TV LOTTO $30.00
Ideal, 1961

THREE CHIPMUNKS ACORN HUNT $35.00
Hasbro, 1960

♟ THREE CHIPMUNKS BIG RECORD $35.00
Hasbro, 1960

♟ THREE CHIPMUNKS CROSS COUNTRY GAME $35.00
Hasbro, 1960

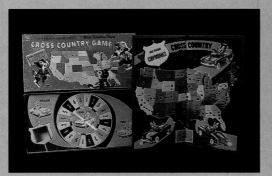

☖ THREE STOOGES FUN HOUSE GAME $200.00
Lowell, 1959
Designer: Julie Cooper
Artwork: Marv Levy

☖ THUNDERBIRDS $60.00
Parker Brothers, 1967
Gerry Anderson's puppetry technique, "supermariona-tion," was used in this British-produced television series.

THUNDERBIRDS $65.00
Waddington, 1965

TOM AND JERRY $11.00
Milton Bradley, 1977

TOM AND JERRY $17.00
Milton Bradley, 1968

TOM AND JERRY $48.00
Parker Brothers, 1948

TOM AND JERRY $37.00
Selchow & Righter, 1962

Designer: Angelo Longo
Set in a kitchen, Jerry had to grab food "goodies" with-out getting caught by Tom.

TOM AND JERRY BOWLING SET $25.00
Transogram, 1966

TOM AND JERRY MAGNETIC FISHING GAME $30.00
Transogram, 1966

TOM AND JERRY PLATTER SPLATTER $36.00
Transogram, 1966
The MGM cat and mouse were featured on small plastic plates that would break apart when hit with the sup-plied ball.

TOM AND JERRY TARGET GAME $30.00
Transogram, 1966
Hit the mallet on the target with your dart gun and Jerry pops out of his hole.

TOM AND JERRY — ADVENTURES IN
   BLUNDERLAND $30.00
Transogram, 1965

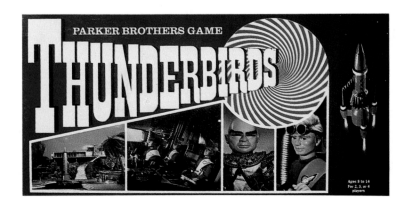

TWINKLES – HIS TRIP TO THE STAR FACTORY $100.00
Milton Bradley, 1961

UNDERDOG $45.00
Milton Bradley, 1964

UNDERDOG'S SAVE SWEET POLLY GAME $30.00
Whitman, 1972

TOP CAT $100.00
Whitman, 1962

TOP CAT SHOE TOSS GAME $125.00
Transogram, 1962
Throw shoes at the plastic figures of Top Cat and his pals.

TOUCHÉ TURTLE $120.00
Transogram, 1962
The original "hero in a half-shell."

WACKY RACES $40.00
Milton Bradley, 1969
Designer: Jim Houlihan

WALLY GATOR $75.00
Transogram, 1962

WALTER LANTZ PICTURE DOMINOES $30.00
Saalfield, 1963
Dominoes contained pictures of Lantz characters such as Andy Panda, Oswald Rabbit, Chilly Willy, and others.

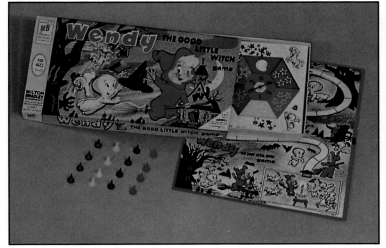

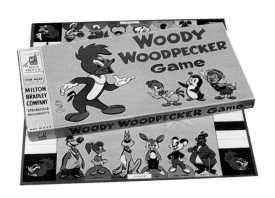

☖ WENDY THE GOOD LITTLE WITCH $165.00
Milton Bradley, 1966
Designer: Bill Burke

WIMPY — WHERE ARE MY HAMBURGERS? $53.00
Hasbro, 1965
Even Popeye's mooching friend had his own game.

WINKY DINK TV KIT $60.00
Pressman, 1955
Kit included the official magic window to draw on your TV screen
and a magic TV game book among others.

WIZARD OF OZ $44.00
Lowell, 1962

WONDER WOMAN, JUSTICE LEAGUE
    OF AMERICA $125.00
Hasbro, 1967

☖ WONDERBUG $25.00
Ideal, 1977

☖ WOODY WOODPECKER $24.00
Milton Bradley, 1958

WOODY WOODPECKER CARD GAME $17.00
Fairchild, 1964

WOODY WOODPECKER CRAZY MIXED-UP
    COLOR FACTORY $20.00
Whitman, 1972

☖ WOODY WOODPECKER'S GAME BOX $25.00
Saalfield, 1964

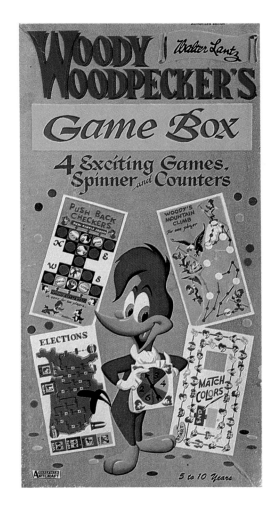

WOODY WOODPECKER'S MOON DASH GAME $15.00
Whitman, 1976

♟ WOODY WOODPECKER, TRAVEL WITH $50.00
Cadaco, 1956

♟ YOGI BEAR $20.00
Milton Bradley, 1971
Designer: Doug Beck

YOGI BEAR & HUCKLEBERRY HOUND
    BOWLING SET $48.00
Transogram, 1960
Set came with 8" plastic pins in the shape of Huck and Yogi.

YOGI BEAR CARD GAME $16.00
Ed-U-Cards, 1961
This price is for the 5½" X 5¼" box. The set that came as a pack of cards is valued at $8.00.

YOGI BEAR CIRCUS BAGATELLE $40.00
Marx, 1960

♟ YOGI BEAR GO FLY A KITE $38.00
Transogram, 1961

YOGI BEAR KNOCK DOWN PITCH GAME $30.00
Transogram, 1960
Came with six 6" plastic figures of Yogi to stack up and knock down.

♟ YOGI BEAR SCORE-A-MATIC BALL TOSS $60.00
Transogram, 1960
When you tossed a ball into Yogi's mouth on this 20" high target, the score-a-matic would register and the ball would be returned to you through a chute in the front.

YOGI BEAR SLING RING TOSS $20.00
Transogram, 1962
Set came with an 18" tall figure of Yogi on roller skates.

NO GIRLS ALLOWED!

The very first war game may have been Chess. It dates back to sixth century India and may represent an abstraction of a battle whose details have been lost in the shifting sands of time. Through the years, the availability of war games runs the spectrum from simple and vague to complex and detailed. All share the common themes of movement of pieces, position of forces, and the capture or annihilation of the opposition. Heavy stuff when you were a kid. Still, it offered some semblance of machismo for boys. Plus, it stopped your creepy sister and her friends from hanging around, as the mere sight of these games usually sent girls running from your clubhouse in terror. Could you outperform Caesar or succeed where Napoleon failed? Somehow, I think we'd all be better off if the world's conflicts could be solved with the roll of the dice or the flip of a chance card.

♟ 12 O'Clock High $45.00
Ideal, 1965
Artwork: Ralph Pereida
When Robert Lansing's character was killed on the show, Ideal replaced his picture with new cast member Paul Burke. That game is valued at $45.00.

♟ 12 O'Clock High Card Game $35.00
Milton Bradley, 1965
Designer: Jim Houlihan

1863 Civil War Game $25.00
Parker Brothers, 1961
Designers: Charles Elliot, Thomas Carmichael, Paul Mandel
The game's three designers were *Life Magazine* editors. The year 1863 was chosen as the setting because at that time the Union and Confederate armies were closely balanced and it was still possible for either side to win.

Air Combat $25.00
Milton Bradley, 1968
Designer: Sol Friedman
Plastic WWI planes extending from two large pylons circled around trying to down the opponent.

Air Empire $25.00
Avalon Hill, 1961

Battle Board $12.00
Ideal, 1972
When you hit down on a plastic pump, a shot of air sent some of your opponents markers flying.

♟ Battle Cry $40.00
Milton Bradley, 1961
Designer: Jim Houlihan
In keeping with Milton Bradley's credo that games should be fun and educational, each of their American Heritage games included a lengthy booklet explaining the background of the historical battle... which kids must have promptly thrown out because you rarely find them in the games.

♟ Battle Line $40.00
Ideal, 1964
Artwork: Ralph Pereida

Battle Stations! $20.00
John Burleson, 1952
Battleship grid game, came with sealed secret orders to align your ships.

♟ BATTLESHIP $7.00
Milton Bradley, 1967
Designer: Ted Starcewski
Real common. Almost everyone has one of these in
their attic somewhere.

♟ BATTLESHIP $55.00
Whitman, 1940

BEACHHEAD INVASION $38.00
Built-Rite, 1950s

BLAST $10.00
Ideal, 1973

BLITZKRIEG $23.00
Avalon Hill, 1965

♟ BROADSIDE $35.00
Milton Bradley, 1962
Designer: Jim Houlihan
Another in the series of Milton Bradley's American Her-
itage games. This one was based on the War of 1812.

♟ BRUCE FORCE & THE TREASURE OF
        SHARK ISLAND $40.00
Ideal, 1963
This Ideal envelope game had Mr. Force combing an
underwater cave in search of treasure belonging to
Barton the Bloodthirsty.

♟ CAMELOT $16.00

Parker Brothers, 1961

Designer: George S. Parker

In his goal to produce a game more complex than Checkers, but not as difficult as Chess, Parker Brothers founder, George Parker, created what he called "the best game in 2,000 years"— Chivalry. After it met with limited success, Parker re-released it with new rules and called it Camelot. It had very good success for many years.

CAMPAIGN $46.00

Saalfield, 1961

This Civil War entry from Saalfield was subtitled "The American 'Go' Game."

♟ CAPTURE HILL 79 $55.00

Hasbro, 1968

This G.I. Joe game had cards that when soaked in water determined your move. Because of that, finding a mint copy is tough!

CARRIER STRIKE! $20.00

Milton Bradley, 1977

CHOPPER STRIKE $18.00

Milton Bradley, 1976

♟ CIVIL WAR $30.00

Milton Bradley, 1961

Designer: Jim Houlihan

♟ COMBAT $35.00

Ideal, 1963

Artwork: Ralph Pereida

During this show's five-year run, merchandise for the popular series starring Rick Jason and Vic Morrow ranged from guns and grenades to these three games by Ideal.

♟ COMBAT AT ANZIO
BEACHEAD $50.00
Ideal, 1963 *(Page 94)*

♟ COMBAT CARD GAME $30.00
Milton Bradley, 1965
Designer: Jim Houlihan *(Page 94)*

COMBAT TANK ATTACK $25.00
Tarco, 1965
Artwork: Ron Vitale

CONFLICT $30.00
Parker Brothers, 1960
Artwork: Jack McMann
This game is collectible because it was filled with many metal ships, planes, and cannon. The 1940s version had composition pieces and is valued at $95.00.

CONVOY $20.00
Transogram, 1968
Another Battleship-type grid game, it came in two versions, one had two separate playing boards, and a smaller version contained one single board that two people would play on.

DIPLOMACY $20.00
Games Research, 1971

DIRECT HIT $65.00
Northwestern, 1950
This was a target game where dart bombs were dropped from a plane to a cityscape below.

♟ DOGFIGHT $35.00
Milton Bradley, 1962
Designer: Jim Houlihan
Another of Milton Bradley's American Heritage games. This one was based on WWI flying aces.

DOMINATION $15.00
Milton Bradley, 1960s
Designer: Sid Sackson
Sackson's daughter wanted him to choose another name for his war game. She thought it symbolized men dominating women.

EXPANSE $32.00
Milton Bradley, 1940s

♟ FEUDAL $20.00
3M, 1969

FIGHTER BOMBER $25.00
Cadaco, 1977

FLYING ACES $50.00
Selchow & Righter, 1948
Dogfights galore!

♟ FLYING THE BEAM $60.00
Parker Brothers, 1941
Designer: William Chapman
Developed by an officer in the U.S. Air Force. You were close to home when you passed through the "Twilight Zones" and flew over the "Cone of Silence."

FOIL $10.00
3M, 1969

G.I. JOE CARD GAME $18.00
Whitman, 1965

⚬ G.I. JOE COMBAT INFANTRY GAME $45.00
Hasbro, 1965

⚬ G.I. JOE MARINE PARATROOP! GAME $40.00
Hasbro, 1965

⚬ G.I. JOE NAVY FROGMAN GAME $60.00
Hasbro, 1965

G.I. JOE RIK-O-SHAY GAME $48.00
Hasbro, 1965

GARRISON'S GORILLAS $70.00
Ideal, 1967
Artwork: Ralph Pereida

GRAY GHOST $45.00
⚬ *Transogram, 1958*
This television show about a Confederate hero was
released reluctantly at the start of the civil rights
movement. Surprisingly, it did well.

GUIDED MISSILE NAVY GAME $15.00
Milton Bradley, 1964

⚬ HIT THE BEACH $36.00
Milton Bradley, 1962
Designer: Jim Houlihan

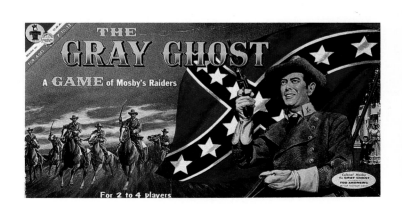

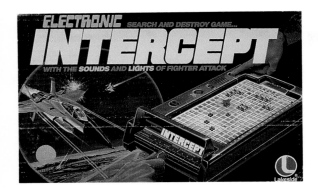

☖ INTERCEPT $22.00
Lakeside, 1978

KARATE MEN FIGHTING ACTION GAME $50.00
Aurora, 1970
Contained two large remote-controlled fighting men.

LET'S GO, JOE $50.00
Hasbro, 1966
Among its many components, this G.I. Joe game contained 12
plastic soldiers, plus Defense & Attack Headquarters.

☖ LIEUTENANT COMBAT TOWN GAME $80.00
Transogram, 1963

MANEUVER $12.00
Cadaco, 1967

MILITARY CHESS $12.00
Cossman, 1959

PHALANX $24.00
Whitman, 1964

POW CANNON GAME $25.00
Milton Bradley, 1964
Designer: Marvin Glass & Assoc.

☖ PT BOAT 109 $30.00
Ideal, 1963
Artwork: Ralph Pereida
This game was based on the Kennedy fervor of the time.

☖ PURSUIT $25.00
Aurora, 1973

☖ RADAR SEARCH $23.00
Ideal, 1969
Designer: Kenneth Parker
Ideal's game of strategy and international espionage on
the high seas was equipped with the "latest navigational
instruments" a radar and anti-radar device.

♟ RAT PATROL $48.00
Transogram, 1966
Based on TV's Allied Unit in North Africa during World
War II, this game had a plastic overlay to help you plot
the next attack.

♟ RAT PATROL SPIN TO WIN GAME $50.00
Pressman, 1967

RATTLE BATTLE $8.00
Parker Brothers, 1970
Designer: Marvin Glass & Assoc.
Ideal, 1967

♟ RISK $20.00
Parker Brothers, 1959
Later versions containing plastic pieces are valued at
$7.00 – $10.00.

ROMAN X $15.00
Selchow & Righter, 1964
Players maneuvered as Roman gladiators on the board.
The game also included "Thumbs Up" and "Thumbs Down"
cards to add just the right amount of suspense.

SALVO $30.00
Ideal, 1961

♟ SIEGE $32.00
Milton Bradley, 1966
Suggested by Stan Weston
Designer: Jim Houlihan
This was a game Bradley put out for Sears. Although it
was neat looking, it was a big bust.

SKIRMISH $30.00
Milton Bradley, 1975

♟ SONAR SUB HUNT $60.00
Mattel, 1961

♟ STRATEGIC COMMAND $40.00
Transogram, 1962
Designer: Sol Friedman
Magnetic playing pieces repelled each other when placed on directly opposite sides of the board, allowing players to knock-out opponent's forces and capture the enemy headquarters.

♟ STRATEGO $15.00
Milton Bradley, 1961
Designers: Houseman & Hotte
The instructions insist it isn't a war game, then describe "bombs which blow up and remove any attacking piece." Later versions with plastic instead of wooden pieces are valued at $7.00.

♟ SUB ATTACK $30.00
Milton Bradley, 1965
Suggested by Harvey-Carlson
Designer: Jim Houlihan

♟ SUB SEARCH $23.00
Milton Bradley, 1973
This big three-level game had you maneuver your ships and subs to avoid mines and enemy fire.

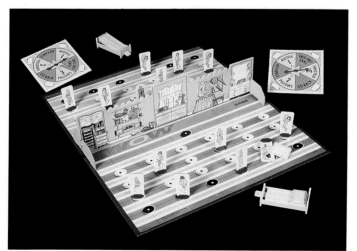

♟ SUMMIT $25.00
Milton Bradley, 1960
Designer: Reuben Klamer
Artwork: Chuck Norman
Milton Bradley president James Shea holds a copy of
their newest war game that relied on diplomacy to win.

♟ SWORDS & SHIELDS $17.00
Milton Bradley, 1970
Designer: Bill Burke

TANK BATTLE $19.00
Milton Bradley, 1975

U.S. AIR FORCE, THE STORY OF THE $45.00
Transogram, 1961
This was based on Random House's Landmark
Book series.

UNDERCOVER $35.00
Cadaco, 1960
Future secret agents mapped their escape
routes, wore infra-scope goggles to simulate
night travel, and trusted the friendly underground
to guide them through enemy defenses.

WEST POINT STORY $40.00
Transogram, 1961
This was based on Random House's Landmark Book
series.

♟ WOW! PILLOW FIGHT $30.00
Milton Bradley, 1964
Designer: Marvin Glass & Assoc.
This is as close as girls got to a war game. Use your
bed to catapult pillows at your opponent's slumber
party guests and the poor unsuspecting housemother.

This is a strange category in that it contains a very diverse group of manufacturers as well as prices. It seems that many people thought they could invent a game that would duplicate the fun, strategy, and excitement of their favorite sport. They usually didn't succeed. Many of these games were produced by small companies and might have been the only item they ever manufactured. With the upsurge in sports memorabilia collectors, prices can sometimes be distorted as well as unreasonably inflated. It's ironic that the highest prices paid for sports games are usually for baseball, which is only surpassed in boredom by golf (another sport in which there were a proliferation of board games). While they weren't high on the collectible food chain for many years, the zeal of the new breed of sports fanatic makes collecting these items a whole different ball game.

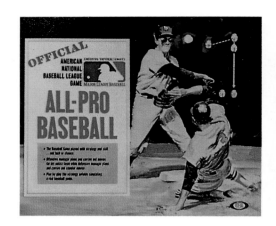

300 MILE RACE $35.00
Built-Rite, 1955

4 QUARTER BASKETBALL GAME $10.00
Built-Rite, 1960s

ACTION BASEBALL $40.00
Pressman, 1964

⚘ ACTION GOLF $20.00
Pressman, 1960s

ALL AMERICAN FOOTBALL $15.00
Cadaco, 1969

⚘ ALL-PRO BASEBALL $15.00
Ideal, 1967
Designer: Julie Cooper

⚘ ALL-PRO BASKETBALL $20.00
Ideal, 1969
Designer: Julie Cooper

⚘ ALL-PRO FOOTBALL $17.00
Ideal, 1967
Designer: Julie Cooper

⚘ ALL-PRO HOCKEY $18.00
Ideal, 1969
Designer: Julie Cooper

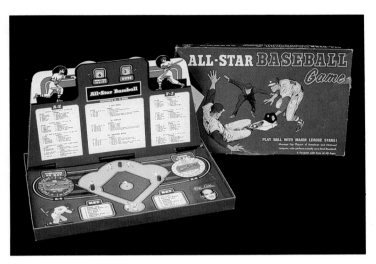

ALL-STAR BOWLING $35.00
Gotham, 1961

ALL-STAR FOOTBALL $18.00
Gardner, 1950s

ALL-STAR BASEBALL, ETHAN ALLEN'S $85.00
Cadaco, 1946
Designer: Ethan Allen
This came with 60 major league player discs so you
could duplicate the actual batting performances of
the pros.

♟ ALL-STAR BASEBALL $30.00
Cadaco, 1953
Designer: Ethan Allen

ALL-STAR BASKETBALL BAGATELLE $55.00
Gotham, 1950

♟ AMERICAN DERBY $35.00
Cadaco, 1951

ARMCHAIR QUARTERBACK $12.00
JRH, 1964

ARMCHAIR QUARTERBACK $15.00
Novelty Mfg., 1955

ARNOLD PALMER'S INDOOR GOLF COURSE $40.00
Marx, 1968

ARNOLD PALMER'S INSIDE GOLF $65.00
Remson, 1962
Forget the weather and play championship golf on
your living-room table.

♟ AURORA DERBY $67.00
Aurora, 1970
Designer: Marvin Glass & Assoc.
Cool game combined pinball and horse racing. Each
time your steel ball was shot up a ramp and into a
hole, your horse moved ahead.

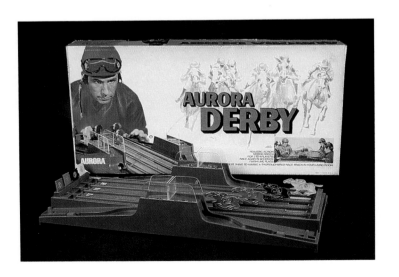

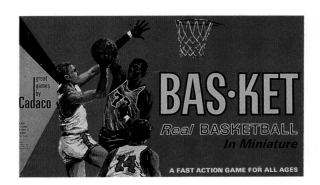

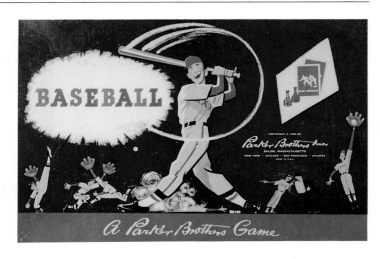

AUTHENTIC MAJOR LEAGUE BASEBALL GAME $8.00
Sports Games Inc., 1962

BABE RUTH'S BASEBALL GAME $225.00
Toy Town, 1940s

♟ BAS-KET $18.00
Cadaco, 1960
Sink a basket from any one of six mechanically con-
trolled levers in this "action-packed game of thrills."

BASEBALL $50.00
All-Fair, 1946

BASEBALL $85.00
Corey, 1943

BASEBALL $55.00
Milton Bradley, 1941

♟ BASEBALL $30.00
Parker Brothers, 1959
Parker Brothers claimed this game was designed to create the thrill and psychology of the duel between pitcher
and batter.

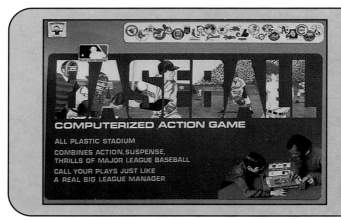

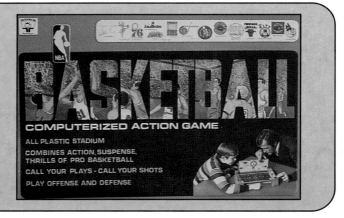

♟ BASEBALL $25.00
Transogram, 1969

♟ BASKETBALL $25.00
Transogram, 1969

BASKETBALL STRATEGY $13.00
Avalon Hill, 1974

BATTER UP $15.00
Ed-U-Cards, 1949

BIG LEAGUE BASEBALL $20.00
3M, 1966

BIG LEAGUE MANAGER FOOTBALL $17.00
BLM, 1965

ᚼ BING-IT $14.00
Matchbox, 1960s
Designers: Sunny Banks, Sidney Lutzin, John MacEnroe
That's a lot of inventors for a simple game!

BLUE LINE HOCKEY $28.00
3M, 1968

BOB FELLER'S BIG LEAGUE BASEBALL $120.00
Saalfield, 1950s

BOWL AND SCORE $5.00
Lowe, 1962
This was a dice game.

ᚼ BOWL A STRIKE $6.00
Lowe, 1962
Here's another example of Lowe's fascination with turning ten-pins into a dice game.

BOWL-A-MATIC $55.00
Eldon, 1963
A small mechanical bowler shot the ball down this big, four-foot alley.

BOWL BOUND $23.00
Sports Illustrated, 1973

BOWL-EM $18.00
Parker Brothers, 1950s

ᚼ BOWLO $10.00
Feature Games, 1957
This card game let you enjoy all the fun of bowling without having to rent those ugly shoes.

BOX HOCKEY $5.00
Merdel, 1971

BREAK PAR GOLF GAME $30.00
Built-Rite, 1950s

BRUCE JENNER DECATHALON $13.00
Parker Brothers, 1979

BUMP-A-LITE POOL $25.00
Aurora, 1973

CALL IT GOLF $20.00
Strauss, 1966

CARL HUBBELL MECHANICAL BASEBALL $230.00
Gotham, 1948
This 15" x 15" metal game had a spring operated pitcher and batter.

CASEY ON THE MOUND $225.00
Kamm's Games, 1945

CAVALCADE $23.00
Selchow & Righter, 1948
This set came with instructions to play five different race games.

CHALLENGE GOLF AT PEBBLE BEACH $15.00
3M, 1972

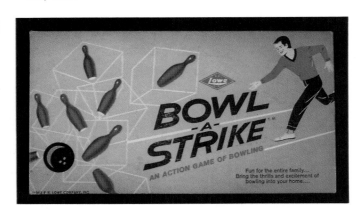

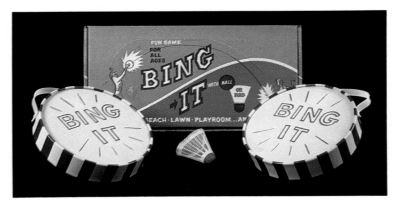

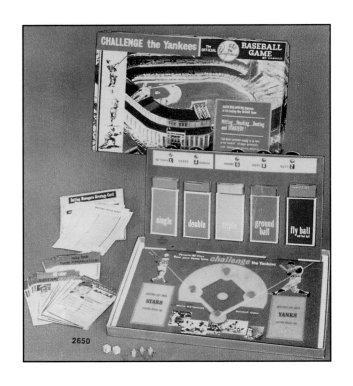

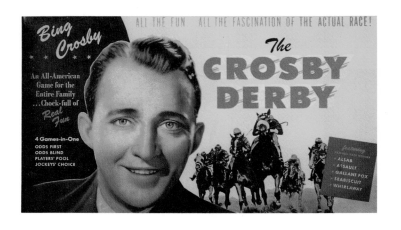

⚲ CHALLENGE THE YANKEES $165.00
Hasbro, 1964

CHAMPION 6 IN 1 SPORTS COMBINATION $22.00
Transogram, 1959
Came with everything from bowling to shuffleboard and golf to darts.

CHAMPIONSHIP BASEBALL $18.00
Championship Games, 1966

CHAMPIONSHIP BASEBALL $30.00
Lansing, 1966

CHAMPIONSHIP BASKETBALL $14.00
Championship Games, 1966

CHAMPIONSHIP GOLF $12.00
Championship Games, 1966

⚲ CHAMPIONSHIP GOLF $20.00
Gardner, 1950s

COLLEGE BASKETBALL $15.00
Cadaco, 1954

⚲ CROSBY DERBY $60.00
Fishlove, 1947
Der Bingle's obsession with the ponies led to this game. Maybe he thought it would entice players to try their hand at a real race track, such as California's Del Mar, of which Crosby was part owner.

DAN KERSTETER'S CLASSIC FOOTBALL $15.00
Big League Game Co., 1971

DECATHALON $12.00
Sports Illustrated, 1972

DERBY DOWNS $19.00
Great Games, 1973
This game came with a record that played the outcome of races you would bet on.

DOG RACE $32.00
Transogram, 1951

EARL GILLESPIE BASEBALL GAME	$30.00	ELECTRIC BASKETBALL	$30.00
Wei-Gill, 1961		*Electric Game Co., 1940s*	
		Designer: Jim Prentice	

EDDIE ARCARO HORSE RACE $30.00
Transogram, 1962
This had all the pulse-pounding excitement of the sport
of kings as you could get on a flat board.

⚇ ELECTRIC FOOTBALL $22.00
Electric Game Co., 1940s
Designer: Jim Prentice

⚇ ELECTRIC BASEBALL $30.00
Electric Game Co., 1940s
Designer: Jim Prentice

ELECTRIC HOCKEY $24.00
Electric Game Co., 1950s
Designer: Jim Prentice

ELECTRIC SPEEDWAY $25.00
Electric Game Co., 1961
Designer: Jim Prentice

ELECTRIC WHIZ RACEWAY $15.00
Electric Game Co., 1961
Designer: Jim Prentice

EMPIRE AUTO RACES $25.00
Empire Plastics, 1950s

EXTRA INNINGS $10.00
Kavanaugh, 1975

⚇ FAIRWAY GOLF $30.00
Trio, 1954

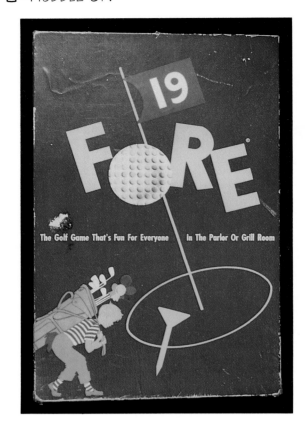

FOOTBALL *All-Fair, 1946*	$45.00
♀ FORE *Artcraft Paper Products, 1954*	$15.00
♀ FORMULA 1 *Parker Brothers, 1963* *Artwork: Jack McMann* Not showing enough action, McMann re-worked the cover using a photo of an actual car race.	$37.00
FOTO-ELECTRIC BASEBALL *Cadaco, 1950*	$25.00
♀ FOTO-ELECTRIC FOOTBALL *Cadaco, 1950* The 1946 wooden version is valued at $35.00.	$12.00
FOUR LANE ROAD RACING GAME *Transogram, 1964*	$20.00
FRANK CAVANAUGH'S AMERICAN FOOTBALL *Cavanaugh Assoc., 1955*	$30.00
GIANT WHEEL HOT ROD GAME *Remco, 1960* Remco's series of wheel games came with a 12" plastic roulette wheel and 48" gameboards.	$50.00
GIANT WHEEL SPEED BOAT GAME *Remco, 1960*	$55.00
♀ GIANT WHEEL THRILLS & SPILLS HORSE RACE GAME *Remco, 1958*	$65.00

GILL HODGES' PENNANT FEVER $50.00
Research Games, 1970

GOLFERINO $60.00
Hubley, 1963
Designer: Marvin Glass & Assoc.
There were bridges, tunnels, sand traps, and hazards to make this three-dimensional game a real challenge. This game was re-released ten years later by Milton Bradley and called Pivot Golf.

GRAND PRIX $16.00
Amsco, 1966
Plastic cars with steel balls underneath would race down a four foot figure "8" track.

HERMAN HICKMAN'S ACTION FOOTBALL $60.00
Lowell, 1954
Mechanical kicker actually kicked field goals and extra points. The game also included a booklet that described plays used in college and the pros.

HOCKEY $30.00
Cadaco, 1958

HOME STRETCH, THE $11.00
Hasbro, 1970

HOME TEAM BASEBALL $35.00
Selchow & Righter, 1957
Selchow & Righter claimed that every known play in National Baseball can be made with this game.

HOT WHEELS WIPEOUT GAME $35.00
Mattel, 1968

HUGGIN' THE RAIL $60.00
Selchow & Righter, 1948

INTERNATIONAL GRAND PRIX $20.00
Magic Wand, 1964

JACKIE ROBINSON BASEBALL GAME $275.00
Gotham, 1950s

JERRY KRAMER'S INSTANT REPLAY $15.00
EMD Enterprises, 1970

JIMMY THE GREEK ODDSMAKER BASKETBALL $10.00
Aurora, 1974

JIMMY THE GREEK ODDSMAKER FOOTBALL $10.00
Aurora, 1974

JOHNNY UNITAS FOOTBALL $75.00
Pro Mentor, 1970

  & JUNIOR QUARTERBACK $10.00
Built-Rite, 1960s

  & JUNIOR TABLE TOP BOWLING ALLEY $20.00
Merit, 1961

KENTUCKY DERBY HORSE RACING GAME $14.00
Whitman, 1969

KING PIN DELUXE BOWLING ALLEY $24.00
Baldwin, 1947

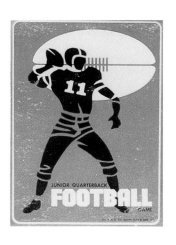

KNOCKOUT $125.00
Northwestern, 1950
This boxing game had two plastic heavyweights going at
it. It also came complete with a ringside bell.

KNUCKLE BUSTERS $50.00
Hasbro, 1967
Taking a cue from Marx's Rock 'em Sock 'em Robots,
Hasbro's fighters had noses that lit up when a hit was
scored. Also came with a 45-rpm record containing ring-
side sounds.

KROKAY $28.00
Transogram, 1955
This was simply a regulation croquet set with a different
spelling of the popular outdoor game.

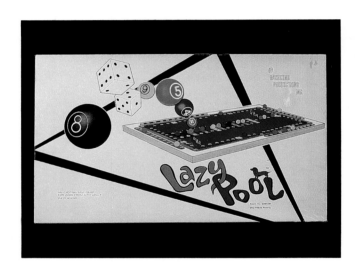

♟ LAZY POOL $5.00
Dashound, 1965

LET'S BOWL A GAME $10.00
D.M.R., 1960

LET'S PLAY BASEBALL $15.00
D.M.R., 1965

LET'S PLAY BASKETBALL $10.00
D.M.R., 1965

LET'S PLAY GOLF $10.00
D.M.R., 1963

LET'S PLAY GOLF: THE HAWAIIAN OPEN $20.00
Burlu, 1968

LITTLE LEAGUE BASEBALL $55.00
Standard Toykraft, 1950s

LONG BALL $22.00
Ashburn, 1975

LONG SHOT $55.00
Parker Brothers, 1962

LOS ANGELES DODGERS GAME $45.00
Ed-U-Cards, 1964

♟ LUCKY '9' RACE GAME $20.00
Built-Rite, 1956
This had the "Dude Ranch" game on the other side of
the board.

MAGIC AUTO RACE $15.00
1952
Colorfully lithographed vibrating speedway sent autos
racing with the flick of a handle.

MAJOR LEAGUE BASEBALL $15.00
Cadaco, 1965

MATCH POINT TENNIS $8.00
Cadaco, 1971
A variation of Cadaco's Bas-ket where levers flipped the
ball into the net. This version had two tennis rackets at
center court to block your opponents shots.

Manage Your Own Baseball
   Team $40.00
Built-Rite, 1955

♟ Mel Allen's Baseball
   Game $50.00
RCA, 1959
This was a 33⅓-rpm record full of baseball calls that you listened to as you played the game on the back of the album.

Mets Baseball Card
   Game $40.00
Ed-U-Cards, 1961

Mickey Mantle's Big League
   Baseball $140.00
Gardner, 1955

♟ Monday Morning Quarterback
Zbinden, 1963 $17.00

Monday Night
   Baseball $35.00
Aurora, 1973

Monday Night Football with
   Roger Staubach $35.00
Aurora, 1973

Motorace $35.00
Ewing, 1955

National Pro Football
   Hall of Fame $15.00
Cadaco, 1965

NBA All-Pro Basketball $20.00
Ideal, 1969

NBC Game of the Week $18.00
Hasbro, 1969

NBC Pro Playoff $16.00
Hasbro, 1969

NFL All-Pro Football $22.00
Ideal, 1967

NFL Strategy $15.00
Tudor, 1978
Tudor came a long way from their electric football sets to this complicated, strategy game.

NHL All-Pro Hockey $15.00
Ideal, 1969

Nok Hockey $40.00
Carrom, 1947

♟ Nuttsy Tennis $7.00
Tomy, 1974
Two spring-activated racquets sent a counterbalanced ball across the court.

O.J. Simpson See Action
   Football $80.00
Kenner, 1974
A cross between the Give-A-Show projector and a sports game. This game's value rose dramatically in mid-1994 for obvious reasons.

Official Baseball Card
   Game $200.00
Milton Bradley, 1953
Contained some rare baseball cards from the 1950s.

Official Baseball Card
   Game $60.00
Milton Bradley, 1970

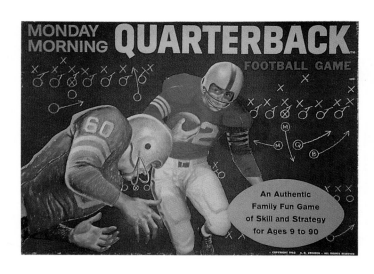

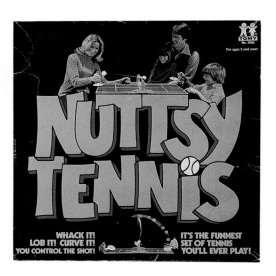

⚲ Official Baseball Game $140.00
Milton Bradley, 1966

Official Globetrotter Basketball, The $100.00
Meljak, 1950s

Official NFL Football Game $30.00
Ideal, 1968

Par 73 $18.00
Big Top, 1961

Par Golf $20.00
Grimes, 1959

Par Golf $35.00
National Games, 1950s

Paul Brown's Football Game $150.00
Trikilis, 1947

Paydirt $10.00
Sports Illustrated, 1973

PD Cue Bumper Pool $35.00
Milton Bradley, 1973
Designer: Marvin Glass & Assoc.

Pennant Chasers Baseball Game $50.00
Hopkins, 1946

Phil & Tony Esposito's Action Hockey $50.00
Parker Brothers, 1973
Designer: Marvin Glass & Assoc.

Pigskin $60.00
Parker Brothers, 1946

⚲ Pivot Golf $45.00
Milton Bradley, 1973
Designers: Marvin Glass & Assoc.
This game was released ten years earlier as Golferino by Hubley.

⚲ Pivot Pool $22.00
Milton Bradley, 1972
Designers: Marvin Glass & Assoc.
A cue ball was set on a pivoting shooter and could be adjusted for soft or hard shots.

Play Back $25.00
1971
Here was a ping pong partner that never got tired and returned all your serves. When you hit the ball against the play back screen, it would fall into a pitching mechanism and toss it back at you.

Play Ball Hockey $35.00
Toymasters, 1960
Players rolled marbles down ramps instead of using sticks to knock the puck into the goal.

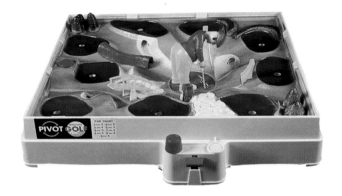

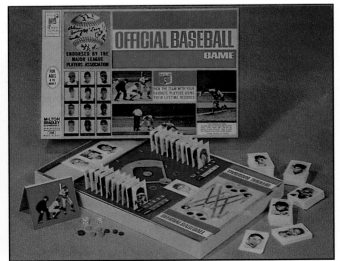

PLAY BASKETBALL WITH BOB COUSY *National Games, 1950s*	$200.00	PRO FOOTBALL *Milton Bradley, 1964*	$30.00
PLYMOUTH DRAG RACE GAME *Day, 1967*	$25.00	⚖ PRO LEAGUE BASKETBALL *Gotham, 1958* You know this one's old — all the players are white!	$75.00
POWER 4 CAR RACE *Zipees, 1964*	$23.00	PRO LOCKER BASEBALL *Fairchild, 1960*	$12.00
⚖ PRO BOWLING *Milton Bradley, 1962*	$30.00	PRO LOCKER FOOTBALL *Fairchild, 1960*	$12.00
⚖ PRO DRAFT *Parker Brothers, 1974*	$32.00	PRO QUARTERBACK *Championship Games, 1965*	$18.00
PRO FOOTBALL *3M, 1966*	$17.00	PRO QUARTERBACK *Lansing, 1964*	$15.00

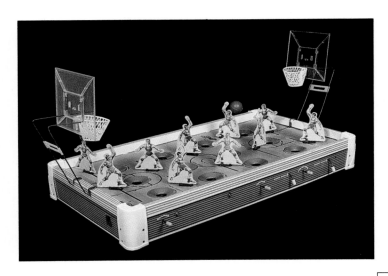

⚑ PRO SOCCER $14.00
Milton Bradley, 1968

⚑ QUARTERBACK $25.00
Transogram, 1969
Forget that crummy, sturdy metal. This game boasted
an all plastic stadium.

QUICKFLIP VOLLEYBALL GAME $15.00
Ideal, 1973

RACE A CAR $35.00
Transogram, 1961
Players flipped a ball into a hole to move their cars
ahead. It was re-released in 1966 as Auto Drome.

RACE TRAP $40.00
Multiple Toymakers, 1960s
Players used sticks to guide "Wild Willy" in his
motorized car through a gateway for points.

RACE-O-RAMA $15.00
Built-Rite, 1960s

RACEWAY $30.00
B&B, 1950s

RAMS FOOTBALL $30.00
Zondine, 1948
The small Los Angeles based company pub-
lished this game for their new home team.

RAZZLE DAZZLE FOOTBALL GAME $36.00
Texantics, 1954

REAL ACTION BASEBALL $20.00
Real Action Games, 1966

REAL-LIFE BASKETBALL $8.00
Gamecraft, 1974

REGATTA $14.00
3M, 1967
Designer: Frank Thibault

RIDE THE SURF $60.00
Surfing Magazine, 1963

ROCKY COLAVITO BASEBALL-BOWLING BALL
     DART GAME $65.00
Transogram, 1960
The Cleveland Indians star outfielder lent his name and
face to this suction cup dart game. The following year,
the game was printed without his name and face.

ROLLER DERBY $22.00
Milton Bradley, 1974

ROSE BOWL $25.00
Lowe, 1966

SAMSONITE BASKETBALL $12.00
Samsonite, 1969

SAMSONITE FOOTBALL $10.00
Samsonite, 1969

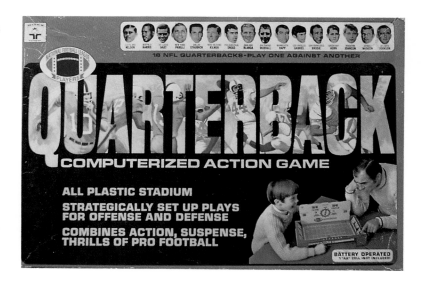

♟ SANDLOT SLUGGER $24.00
Milton Bradley, 1968
Designer: Marvin Glass & Assoc.
Played just like regular baseball, but indoors. It came with a 12" high "Slugging Sam" who hit a baseball on a tee.

SKIN DIVERS $32.00
Ideal, 1961
One of Ideal's Big Bopper games. When you hit the bopper, a ball went up on a string to indicate how far you would submerge to gather sunken treasure.

SKITTLE BASEBALL $35.00
Aurora, 1973
Designer: Eddy Goldfarb

SNAP BOWLING $30.00
Ideal, 1973
Designer: Marvin Glass & Assoc.

SOOPERBOWL $10.00
Sportswise Inc., 1967

SPARE-TIME BOWLING $10.00
Lakeside, 1974

SPARETIME BOWLING $10.00
Schaper, 1959

♟ SPECIAL DETECTIVE/SPEEDWAY $28.00
Saalfield, 1959

SPEED CIRCUIT $16.00
3M, 1971

SPEED-O-RAMA $40.00
Jacmar, 1950s
Four games in one conveying speed on land, sea, and in the air.

♟ SPEEDWAY $32.00
Ideal, 1961
When you hit the bopper, the ball went up on a string to indicate how far you would move your car.

♟ SPORTS ARENA $50.00
Milton Bradley, 1962

SPORTS ILLUSTRATED BASEBALL $15.00
Sports Illustrated, 1972

♟ SPRINT DRAG RACE GAME $32.00
Mattel, 1965

ST. LOUIS CARDINALS BASEBALL GAME $25.00
Ed-U-Cards, 1964

STOCK CAR RACING GAME $25.00
Whitman, 1956

STOCK CAR ROAD RACE $24.00
Gabriel, 1956

STRATEGY MANAGER BASEBALL $20.00
McGuffin-Ramsey, 1967

STRIKE BOWLING $25.00
Hasbro, 1958

♟ SUPER SUNDAY FOOTBALL $30.00
Hasbro, 1973
Designer: Marvin Glass & Assoc.
Game contained a projector that offense and defense film
strips were placed in to see the outcome of the play.

SUPERSTAR BASEBALL $16.00
Sports Illustrated, 1966

SURE SHOT BASEBALL $15.00
Ideal, 1970
Designer: Marvin Glass & Assoc.

SURE SHOT BASKETBALL $15.00
Ideal, 1970
Designer: Marvin Glass & Assoc.

SURE SHOT HOCKEY $15.00
Ideal, 1969
Designer: Marvin Glass & Assoc.

SWEEPSTAKES ELECTROMATIC HORSE RACE $30.00
WM, 1970

SWISH! BASKETBALL GAME $15.00
Built-Rite, 1955

TABLE TOP BOWLING ALLEY $25.00
Merit, 1958

TALKING FOOTBALL $20.00
Mattel, 1971

♟ TALKING MONDAY NIGHT FOOTBALL $20.00
Mattel, 1977

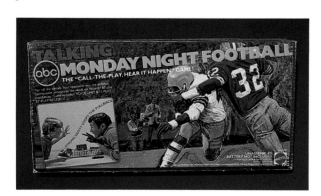

♟ Tee Party *Milton Bradley, 1968*	$22.00	Top Ten Bowling *Parker Brothers, 1963*	$20.00
Thinking Man's Football *3M, 1969*	$15.00	Track Meet *Sports Illustrated, 1972*	$10.00
Thinking Man's Golf *3M, 1966*	$20.00	Trap Tennis *Ideal, 1975*	$8.00
Tiny Tethered Table Tennis *Atech, 1969*	$10.00	Tru-Action Electric Baseball *Tudor, 1960s*	$30.00

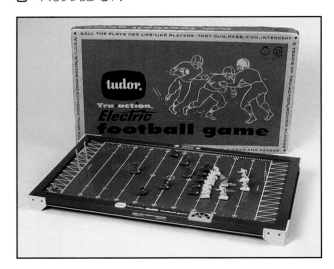

♟ TRU-ACTION ELECTRIC FOOTBALL $24.00
Tudor, 1960
The timer hardly worked, the linebackers would lock arms and dance in circles, and the quarterback could never complete a pass with that little cotton football, but because NFL playoffs coincided with the Christmas season, every boy just had to have one under his tree.

TRU-ACTION ELECTRIC HORSERACE $30.00
Tudor, 1959

♟ TRU-ACTION ELECTRIC SPORTS CAR RACE $30.00
Tudor, 1959

VARSITY $20.00
Cadaco, 1955
Football was the varsity sport referred to in this game.

VINCE LOMBARDI'S GAME $33.00
Research Games, 1970

♟ WIDE WORLD OF SPORTS — AUTO RACING $12.00
Milton Bradley, 1974

♟ WIDE WORLD OF SPORTS — GOLF $12.00
Milton Bradley, 1974

♟ WIDE WORLD OF SPORTS — TENNIS $12.00
Milton Bradley, 1974

WIN, PLACE & SHOW $16.00
3M, 1966

WIN, PLACE & SHOW $40.00
Milton Bradley, 1949

WORLD SERIES $85.00
Lowe, 1947

YACHT RACE $65.00
Parker Brothers, 1961

THE REAL WORLD

"And what do you want to be when you grow up?" If I had a dime for everytime I heard that as a kid, I'd be able to afford some of the things in here. At some point in our childhood we all wanted to act grown up, and what better way than to play games based on what our moms, dads, relatives, and friends' parents did for a living? Hey, you think it's soooo easy to support a family? Well here's five thousand bucks, let's see what you can do with it. This chapter focuses on games about business, careers, and grown-up stuff in general.

⚒ 4 ALARM $18.00
Milton Bradley, 1963

⚒ ACME CHECKOUT GAME $35.00
Milton Bradley, 1959
Designer: Jim O'Connor
Shop through Milton Bradley's simulated store with
cards featuring actual products of the day.

ACQUIRE $20.00
3M, 1962
Designer: Sid Sackson
This was one of inventor Sackson's bigger successes.

AIR TRAFFIC CONTROLLER $17.00
Schaper, 1974

ANALYSIS $13.00
Transogram, 1968
One of Transogram's few adult-themed games
was released under the TAG (Transogram
Adult Games) logo. It contained mock psychi-
atry that "let you love, hate, desire, lust, kill,
and destroy without feeling guilty." The first
to get rid of his neurosis was declared normal
and the winner.

ASSEMBLY LINE $35.00
Selchow & Righter, 1953
This game let you assemble cars like the
motor czars.

AUCTIONEER $14.00
Ideal, 1972

⚒ B.T.O. (BIG TIME OPERATOR) $40.00
Bettye B., 1956
This three-dimensional vacuformed business
game let you buy and sell landmarks of New York
such as Coney Island, the Statue of Liberty, and
Times Square.

BAZAAR $10.00
3M, 1967

BEAT INFLATION $20.00
Avalon Hill, 1961

BEAT THE DRAFT $25.00
1960s
Designer: Frank Thibault
With its fluorescent board, this was billed as the first
black-light game.

BET A MILLION $20.00
Lowe, 1950s

BIG BOARD $20.00
Dadan, 1958
This game was based on playing the stock market.

BIG BOARD FOR JUNIORS $18.00
Dadan, 1962

BIG BOARD $5.00
Eskay Co., 1975

♟ BIG BUSINESS $15.00
Transogram, 1959
Transogram's staple. It was in their catalog for over 20
years. Picture shows 1959 & 1964 covers.

BIG FUNERAL $28.00
1964
Designer: Frank Thibault

BILLIONAIRE $25.00
Happy Hour, 1956
This was a small vacuformed game where you had to
search for uranium to make your fortune.

BILLIONAIRE $10.00
Parker Brothers, 1973
Designer: Marvin Glass & Assoc.

♟ BLACKS AND WHITES $15.00
Psychology Today, 1971

BLUE CHIP STOCK MARKET GAME $17.00
Tech Ventures, 1958

BOOM OR BUST $85.00
Parker Brothers, 1951
In this game, players bought and sold properties. A
unique removable panel in the center of the board dic-
tated Boom or Bust conditions causing prices to rise
and fall.

BOONDOGGLE $30.00
Selchow & Righter, 1952
This political game had players running for office in the
Soap Box, High Hat, Powwow, and Boondoggle Parties.

BOSS, THE $15.00
Ideal, 1972
Designer: Marvin Glass & Assoc.

BROKER $10.00
Murray Corp., 1965

BUILDING BOOM $15.00
Kohner, 1950

♟ BUY AND SELL $10.00
Whitman, 1953

CABBY $55.00
Selchow & Righter, 1950s
Who could get their taxi to the depot first was the object of this game that many collectors seem to remember from their youth, thus commanding a higher price than usual.

CALL KELLY $13.00
Games For Industry, 1966
This was a promotional game put out by the temp agency, Kelly Girls.

CAMPAIGN: GAME OF AMERICAN POLITICS $12.00
Campaign, 1966

♟ CAREERS $15.00
Parker Brothers, 1958
A 1965 version with a different cover is valued at $7.00.

♟ CARGOES $45.00
Selchow & Righter, 1940s
Artwork: William Longyear

♟ CARGOES $23.00
Selchow & Righter, 1958

CHARGE IT $12.00
Whitman, 1972

CHUG-A-LUG DRINKING PARTY GAME $7.00
Dynamic, 1969

CHUTZPA $20.00
Whatchamacallit, 1967

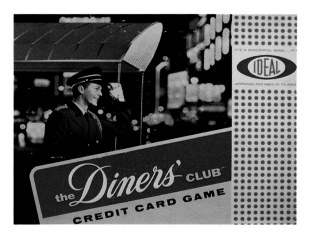

CROSS ROADS $12.00
Selchow & Righter, 1962
Players had to plan a community by taking empty lots
and creating subdivisions on them. It came with over
$125,000 in play money... that's just about what it
takes nowadays to build a shed in the backyard.

♟ DEALERS CHOICE $15.00
Parker Brothers, 1972
Designer: Marvin Glass

DEAR ABBY $15.00
Ideal, 1972
You won this game by guessing what advice Abby would
give to certain problems.

♟ DINER'S CLUB $24.00
Ideal, 1961
Based upon the operation of the country's then leading
credit card plan, this game involved the intricacies of building a credit rating by constantly maneuvering your capital in
order to own a car, a home, and a large bank account. Once
you received your Diner's Club card, you no longer paid cash
for anything and put your money to work by investing it.

DOCTOR QUACK $15.00
Selchow & Righter, 1961
This and Mechanic Mac were added to the perennial S & R
career games line but were discontinued a few years later.

DRIVE-IN $45.00
Selchow & Righter, 1948
Each player had a board containing a replica of a drive-
in on it. Money was made by showing certain movies,
selling ads in between features, and of course...pushing
those concessions!

DRIVER ED $10.00
Cadaco, 1973

♟ EASY MONEY $18.00
Milton Bradley, 1956

♟ ELECTION '68 $25.00
Createk, 1967
It was bad enough we had to listen to their ramblings,
now we had to try and think like 'em in this game.

ELECTRIC WHIZ FIRE FIGHTERS		$15.00

Electric Game Co., 1961
Designer: Jim Prentice

♟ ENGINEER $15.00

Selchow & Righter, 1957
A game for youngsters who want to make the career choice of railroad conductor.

ESCORT $25.00

Parker Brothers, 1955
Escort had players portraying the roles of "guys" trying to escort their "gals" home. It had a plain looking board and playing pieces.

EXECUTIVE DECISION $10.00

3M, 1971
Designer: Sid Sackson

EXPLORATION $10.00

Spiring, 1967

♟ FAME AND FORTUNE $14.00

Whitman, 1962

♟ FEARLESS FIREMAN $80.00

Hasbro, 1957

♟ FINANCE $18.00

Parker Brothers, 1962

FINANCE AND FORTUNE $25.00

Parker Brothers, 1936

FIRE CHIEF $10.00

Selchow & Righter, 1957

FIRE FIGHTERS $20.00

Saalfield, 1957

☖ FLASH: THE PRESS
  PHOTOGRAPHER GAME $65.00
Selchow & Righter, 1956
Designer: Julie Cooper
Players were photographers and
were assigned to bring back pictures of accidents, robberies,
floods, etc. Clearest and best pictures won the game.

FREDDY THE FIREMAN $18.00
Selchow & Righter, 1966
This was a three-dimensional
punch-out game and activity set.

GAME INVENTOR'S KIT $5.00
Selchow & Righter, 1968
Contained components for many
well-known games and allowed you
to make variations on them.

GAMES PEOPLE PLAY $6.00
Alpsco, 1967

☖ GO FOR BROKE $14.00
Selchow & Righter, 1965
This game just kept heaping money
on you. Only thing was, the winner
was the one who could lose it all
first.

GOING, GOING, GONE $10.00
Milton Bradley, 1975
This was obviously an auction game.

GROUP THERAPY $18.00
Parks Plastic, 1969
Designer: Joseph Schlichter
Artwork: Peter Rauch, Herb Levitt

GUINNESS BOOK OF WORLD
  RECORDS $10.00
Parker Brothers, 1979

GUSHER $75.00
Carrom, 1946

⚲ HAPPINESS $14.00
Milton Bradley, 1972
Designer: Marvin Glass

HOME GAME $40.00
Pressman, 1950

HOW TO SUCCEED $50.00
Hasbro, 1950s
Designer: Reuben Klamer

HOWARD HUGHES $15.00
Family Games, 1972

INVENTORS $15.00
Parker Brothers, 1974
Designer: Marvin Glass
Artwork: Jack McMann
Try to make a million as you acquire inventions, collect royalties, and cope with greedy silent partners.

JR. EXECUTIVE $17.00
Whitman, 1963

JUMBO JET $10.00
Jumbo, 1963

⚲ KENNEDYS $40.00
Transogram, 1962
Designers: Jack Winter, Alfred Harrison

KING OF THE SEA $27.00
Ideal, 1975

⚲ KING OIL $15.00
Milton Bradley, 1974
Designer: Ted Starcewski
Players bought property and drilled for oil on the three-dimensional board.

⚲ KOMMISSAR $25.00
Selchow & Righter, 1966

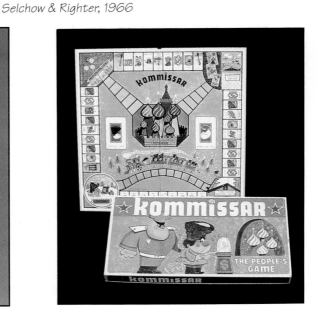

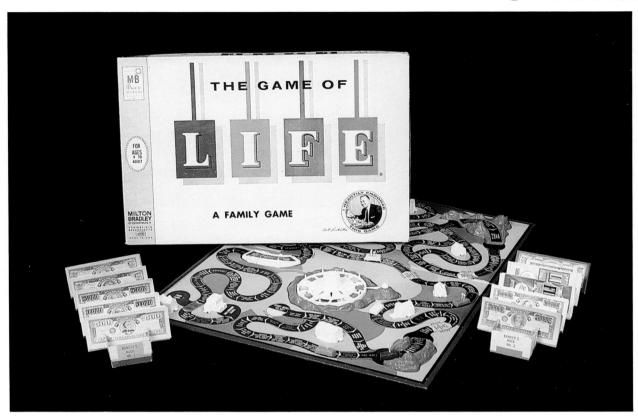

LANDSLIDE $10.00
Parker Brothers, 1971
Designer: Marvin Glass & Assoc.

LIE, CHEAT, AND STEAL $12.00
Reiss, 1976

△ LIFE $10.00
Milton Bradley, 1960
Designers: Reuben Klamer, Bill Markham
Artwork: Eskil Ohlsson

LOBBY $45.00
Milton Bradley, 1949

MAKE A MILLION $10.00
Parker Brothers, 1954

△ MASTERPIECE $9.00
Parker Brothers, 1970
Designer: Marvin Glass & Assoc.
Artwork: Jack McMann
Future art afficionados had to outbid others at an auction while trying to avoid forgeries.

MATING GAME $11.00
Hasbro, 1969
An NBC Home Entertainment game.

MECHANIC MAC $15.00
Selchow & Righter, 1961

△ MERRY MILKMAN $75.00
Hasbro, 1955

MONEY CARD $17.00
Schaper, 1972
This game, subtitled "An American Express Travel Game," taught you how to vacation with your new American Express card and build up lots of credit.

127

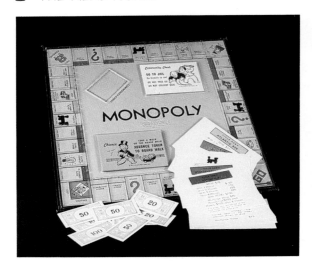

MONEY! MONEY! MONEY! $16.00
Whitman, 1957
Guess what the object of this game was.

♟ MONOPOLY (BRAILLE) $60.00
Parker Brothers, 1972
Designer: Charles Darrow
Since it is the biggest selling game of all time, that also makes it the most common and therefore not always worth a lot. Monopoly was based on an early 1900s game entitled The Landlords Game, invented by Elizabeth Maggie Phillips.

MR. PRESIDENT $12.00
3M, 1967

MY SON THE DOCTOR $6.00
Whatchamacallit, 1969
Enter the world of show-biz, big-biz, politics, and medicine.

NEW FRONTIER $45.00
Colorful Products, 1962
This game was a parody on the Kennedy administration.

NORTHWEST PASSAGE $20.00
Impact Communications, 1969

OPINION POLL $4.00
Selchow & Righter, 1970
Rate traits of fellow players on a scale of 1 to 8 and see who disagrees.

♟ PARK AND SHOP $30.00
Milton Bradley, 1960
Designer: B. Campe Euwer
Euwer, an Allentown, Pennsylvania, newspaperman, modeled this game after the parking system Allentown used to solve a particularly heinous downtown parking problem.

PASS OUT: THE DRINKING GAME $10.00
Pass Out Games Inc., 1962
Designer: Frank Bresee
An uninhibited barroom ball.

♟ PASS OUT TRAVEL EDITION $7.00
Paul Lamond Games, 1976

PAY DAY $6.00
Parker Brothers, 1975

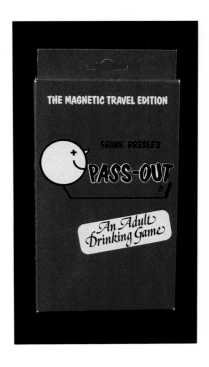

PAY THE CASHIER $15.00
Gilles Widmer, 1957
Designer: Edward Delch
This game taught kids how to make
change at the store.

PETROPOLIS $17.00
Pressman, 1976

POINT OF LAW $10.00
3M, 1972

☖ POLICE PATROL $75.00
Hasbro, 1957

POLICEMAN $35.00
Selchow & Righter, 1957

POLITICS $25.00
Parker Brothers, 1960

POSTMAN $12.00
Selchow & Righter, 1957

☖ PRIZE PROPERTY $20.00
Milton Bradley, 1974
Future real estate tycoons developed neglected
land into hotels, ski lodges, or golf clubs. Watch
out, there were stiff fines for polluting.

PROSPECTING GOLD RUSH GAME $45.00
Selchow & Righter, 1953
Players traveled winding mountain paths
searching for "traces" which might lead to "The
Strike."

PSYCHE-PATHS $10.00
Funtastic, 1969

RICH UNCLE $40.00
Parker Brothers, 1959
Rich Uncle owned the "Daily Bugle" and what that
paper said helped you in your quest to make a fortune. There were also 1962 and 1965 versions of this
game that are valued at $25.00 each.

☖ SCOOP $47.00
Parker Brothers, 1956

⚱ SCREWBALL: A MAD, MAD, MAD GAME $55.00
Transogram, 1960
It's hard to tell from the box, but this is a game about the world of advertising. When *Mad Magazine* threatened to sue for using a character they thought closely resembled Alfred E. Neuman, Transogram changed the cover of their game... slightly! This price is for the cover without the microphone. The box with the microphone is valued at $40.00.

SEDUCTION $13.00
Createk, 1966

SEVEN SEAS $35.00
Cadaco, 1960
Traders competed for profit as they bought and sold cargo around the world.

SHOPPING CENTER $15.00
Whitman, 1957

SIP AND GO NAKED $15.00
Pass Out Games Inc., 1978
Designer: Frank Bresee
The title of this adult game says it all.

SIP AND STRIP $12.00
Pass Out Games Inc., 1978
Designer: Frank Bresee
I think I'm beginning to see a pattern in Mr. Bresee's games.

SMOG $15.00
Urban Systems, 1970

SPIRO T. AGNEW AMERICAN HISTORY
    CHALLENGE GAME $30.00
Gabriel, 1971

SPOT CASH $10.00
Milton Bradley, 1959
Designer: Jim O'Connor

⚱ SQUARE MILE $40.00
Milton Bradley, 1962
Designer: Reuben Klamer
Each player was given a tract of vacant land and tried to develop it into a fortune.

STAMP COLLECTORS GAME $30.00
International, 1970

⚱ STAR REPORTER $45.00
Parker Brothers, 1950s
Each player tried to "scoop" his rivals and become the Star Reporter. Earlier versions of this game are titled "Boak Carter's Star Reporter." Those are valued at $100.00.

STOCK MARKET GAME $27.00
Gabriel, 1956
Buy, sell, and trade utilities, oil,
steel, coal, and gold shares.

STOCK MARKET GAME $18.00
Whitman, 1963

STOCKS & BONDS $15.00
3M, 1964
Designer: Alex Randolph

STRIP TAC TOE $15.00
Diplomat, 1969

SUNKEN TREASURE $17.00
Milton Bradley, 1976

SUNKEN TREASURE GAME $20.00
Parker Brothers, 1948

☖ SUPER MARKET $18.00
Selchow & Righter, 1953
Players were limited to a strict budget which they had to
spend wisely on nutritious food. They also had to obey
traffic signals on the way to the store.

SWAP-WHEELER DEALER GAME $15.00
Ideal, 1965
Designer: Marvin Glass & Assoc.

TAKE IT OFF $8.00
Whatchamacallit, 1969
Game came with a "bump & grind" record that played as

you told jokes and tried to get off stage before the raid
whistle blew. The winner was the first one to lose all of their
clothes (on cards, that is!)

TAXOLOGY $15.00
Gloria Games, 1957

TEST DRIVER $35.00
Milton Bradley, 1957

TEXAS MILLIONAIRE $20.00
Texantics, 1953
This game was sponsored by Neiman Marcus.

TICKER TAPE $22.00
Cadaco, 1963
Buy and sell stocks to gain the most assets. You could
also write in price changes on the "Quote Board" as play
progressed.

TOWN AND COUNTRY TRAFFIC GAME $125.00
Ranger Steel, 1950s

☖ TRANSACTION $10.00
Tusson, 1962
Designer: John R. Tusson

TYCOON $17.00
Parker Brothers, 1966

UNGAME $3.00
Ungame Co., 1975

URANIUM ⚐ $30.00
Saalfield, 1955
Designer: Howard Boughner

URANIUM RUSH ⚐ $100.00
Gardner, 1950s

VEGAS $10.00
Milton Bradley, 1972
Designer: Jim Houlihan

WASH OUT $8.00
Selchow & Righter, 1955
S & R's game about doing laundry.

WATERGATE $15.00
Politico Games, 1973
Designer: George Neal

WATERGATE SCANDAL $20.00
America Symbolic, 1973

WHAT SHALL I BE? $15.00
Selchow & Righter, 1968
S & R put out a girls version and a boys version.

WHITE GLOVE GIRL $15.00
American Publishing, 1966
This game was released as a promo for the maid-for-hire White Glove Girl Company.

WHO CAN BEAT NIXON? $20.00
Dynamic Design, 1970

WILD LIFE ⚐ $17.00
Lowe, 1969
To save the wild animal kingdom from extinction, Lowe had players go on safari to Africa and search the world over for rare species to keep in the zoo.

WINNING TICKET $15.00
Ideal, 1960s
Designer: Sid Sackson

WOMAN AND MAN $8.00
Psychology Today, 1971

WORLD OF WALL STREET $10.00
Hasbro, 1969

ZIP CODE $55.00
Lowell, 1964
Game included cards that resembled letters, a mail box, and Zip Code sorting racks. "Disgruntled postal worker with Uzi" action figure sold separately!

NO BOYS ALLOWED!

The toy industry, for the most part, was run by men making toys for boys. Consequently, games aimed primarily at girls were harder to find than a bottle of Jack Daniels at an AA meeting. In addition, most of the games that were available to the fairer sex also had the point of view of how grown men thought little girls should play. Also, because of their "teeny-bopper nature," rock 'n roll games are included in this episode.

ANGELA CARTWRIGHT'S BUTTONS & BOWS
   GAME $50.00
Transogram, 1960
A game based on "America's little darling as seen on The
Danny Thomas Show."

BABY SITTER $28.00
Ideal, 1966

⚲ BARBIE WORLD OF FASHION $45.00
Mattel, 1967
Barbie, Francie, Casey, and Skipper travel around the
world for modeling fun and fame. The first to return to
London's Carnaby Street with five new dates (little
tramps!) and dresses was the winner.

BARBIE'S KEYS TO FAME $33.00
Mattel, 1963
Girls, like Barbie, could be anything from a movie star to
an astronaut in this game.

⚲ BARBIE, QUEEN OF THE PROM $40.00
Mattel, 1960
A second version of this game was released in 1964 and
contained actual sorority pins instead of cards. It's valued at $45.00.

⚲ BEATLES, FLIP YOUR WIG $100.00
Milton Bradley, 1964
Designers: Jim Houlihan, Jim O'Connor
It's surprising that with all the merchandise produced
around the Fab Four in their heyday, this was the only game.

⚲ BRIDE BINGO $9.00
Leister, 1957

BRIDE GAME $10.00
Selchow & Righter, 1971
Girls went around the board picking up illustrations of
the bride, groom, cake, flowers, etc. in order to have the
perfect wedding.

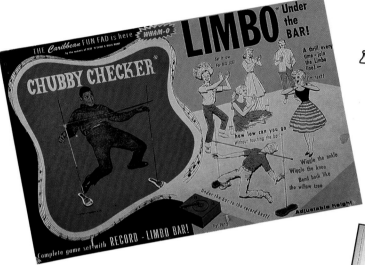

♟ CHUBBY CHECKER'S LIMBO $65.00
Wham-O, 1961
How low can you go? This game came complete with a record of Limbo songs not by Chubby, but by "Kookie Joe."

♟ DREAM DATE $40.00
Transogram, 1963
Transogram's original title for this was "Girl Meets Boy."

♟♟ CAMPUS QUEEN $25.00
King-Seeley, 1967
Artwork: Nick LoBianco
This lunch box came with a spinner and magnetic pieces to play a game that was printed on the back of the box.

CHATTY CATHY GAME $40.00
Mattel, 1962

CHERRY AMES NURSING $48.00
Parker Brothers, 1959
Artwork: Lou Green

CHUBBY CHECKER TWISTER $75.00
Empire Plastics, 1961

CUT UP SHOPPING SPREE $20.00
Milton Bradley, 1969
Designer: Marvin Glass & Assoc.
How about this for the ingredients for a game: kids, scissors, and a timer to see who could use them the fastest. As clothing was being auctioned, girls had to cut out money from sheets as fast as they could to buy the items.

ELVIS PRESLEY $500.00
Teenage Games, 1957

EMILY POST POPULARITY $20.00
Selchow & Righter, 1970
Girls learned the rewards that came from good manners while going to parties, sporting events, etc.

⚲ GIDGET $28.00
Standard Toykraft, 1965

⚲ GIDGET FORTUNE TELLER GAME $30.00
Milton Bradley, 1966
Designer: Jim Houlihan

⚲ HEIDI ELEVATOR GAME $20.00
Remco, 1965

⚲ HULLABALOO ELECTRIC TEEN GAME $60.00
Remco, 1965

⚲ JACKSON 5IVE $45.00
Shindana, 1972
Designer: Eddy Goldfarb

⚲ K-TEL SUPERSTAR GAME $20.00
K-Tel, 1973
Came complete with a record to identify your favorite songs.

KEWPIE DOLL GAME $40.00
Parker Brothers, 1963

KISS ON TOUR $25.00
Aucoin, 1978

♀ LIZ TYLER & THE MYSTERY OF THE
     CROWN JEWELS $30.00
Ideal, 1963
The Liz Tyler games were two of Ideal's six "envelope games."
Originally selling for under a dollar, these games included a
thin, three-color board and four wooden disks. They also
came with a die-cut cardboard sheet containing cards and
a spinner.

♀ LIZ TYLER HOLLYWOOD STARLET $30.00
     Ideal, 1963

MISS AMERICA $18.00
Parker Brothers, 1974
Designer: Marvin Glass & Assoc.
Artwork: Jack McMann

MISS POPULARITY $40.00
Transogram, 1961
Designer: Marvin Glass & Assoc.

♀ MOTHER'S HELPER $20.00
     Milton Bradley, 1969

♀ MONKEES $55.00
Transogram, 1967
Two versions of this game were released. One came with
a plastic guitar and another contained a xylophone.

♀ MYSTERY DATE $48.00
     Milton Bradley, 1965
     Designer: Marvin Glass & Assoc.
     Open the door and find out if your mystery date is taking
          you to a formal dance, a skiing trip, a beach party, or a
          night out bowling. Or as the instructions explain, "Worst
     of all, you may open the door to find the "DUD" and lose
     valuable time in getting rid of him."

⚲ NANCY DREW MYSTERY GAME $65.00
Parker Brothers, 1957
Artwork: Lou Green
A different cover was released in the 1960s
which is valued at $55.00.

⚲ NURSES, THE $27.00
Ideal, 1963
Artwork: Ralph Pereida

⚲ PARTRIDGE FAMILY $25.00
Milton Bradley, 1971

PATTIE PLAYPAL $30.00
Ideal, 1961
Object was to collect six room cards to com-
plete Patti's doll house.

⚲ PATTY DUKE $28.00
Milton Bradley, 1964
Designer: Jim Houlihan
Try to catch those identical cousins, Patty and
Cathy, performing their teenage duties togeth-
er: playing records, watching TV, and dating.

⚲ SENIOR PROM $10.00
Built-Rite, 1966

⚲ SHINDIG $48.00
Remco, 1965

♟ Skipper $23.00
Mattel, 1964
Barbie's little sister had her own game based on "every young girl's dream of owning a horse."

Stork Bingo $4.00
Leister, 1970

Super Group $18.00
Itemation, 1973
Start your own band and see what it's like to work your way up the charts.

♟ Taffy's Baubles & Bangles Game $12.00
Transogram, 1966

♟ Taffy's Party Game $12.00
Transogram, 1966

♟ Taffy's Shopping Spree $12.00
Transogram, 1966

♀ TAMMY $30.00
Ideal, 1963
Artwork: Ralph Pereida

♀ TAMMY CARD GAME $7.00
Whitman, 1964
For some strange reason, Ideal, who made their own card games, licensed out Tammy so Whitman could release a card game of the character created by Ideal.

TINY THUMBELINA $24.00
Ideal, 1963

TINY TIM GAME OF
    BEAUTIFUL THINGS $40.00
Parker Brothers, 1970
Designer: Marvin Glass & Assoc.
With Tiny's appearances on Laugh-In and the Tonight Show, Parker Brothers had high hopes for this one. Unfortunately, it turned out to be one of their biggest bombs.

♀ TWIGGY $33.00
Milton Bradley, 1967

♀ WHAT SHALL I BE? $15.00
Selchow & Righter, 1966
A game for girls looking for career choices. Some cards would tell girls they were "too awkward" to become, say, a model or stewardess.

WHAT SHALL I WEAR? $16.00
Selchow & Righter, 1969

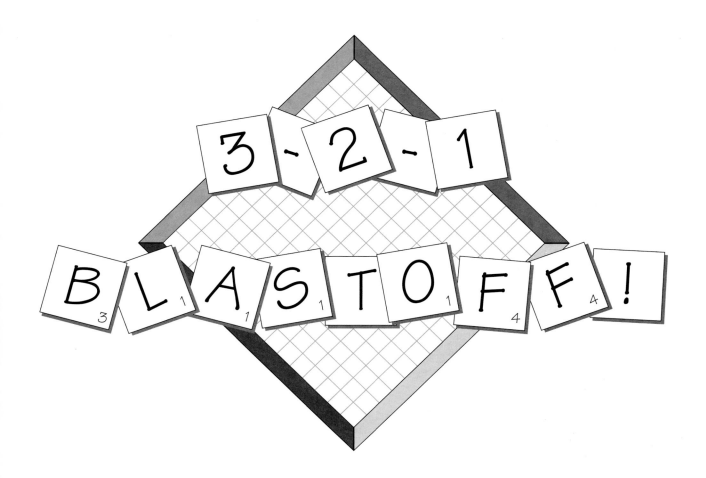

Space. The final frontier. These are the voyages of companies who decided to jump on the bandwagon of the future and promote games about the outer reaches of the universe. Their long-term mission — seek out new customers, explore unknown markets, to boldly go where no game has gone before... in the 99¢ bin at Woolworths. Although they had been on the market for many years, space games weren't embraced by the public until the mid to late 1960s with the excitement and success of the Apollo missions. Hence, some of these babies are rare. Mix that with some of the futuristic designs found on the covers and inside the boxes, and you've got the combination for an out-of-this-world collectible.

☿ ASTRO LAUNCH $70.00
Ohio Art, 1963

☿ BILLY BLASTOFF SPACE GAME $22.00
Danlee, 1969
Artwork: Gunter Schnedel

☿ BUCK ROGERS $65.00
Transogram, 1965
While racing through space, players picked up
Space Kid Delegates to bring to Earth for the
Inter-Planetary Convention. The beautiful art on
the cover doesn't match the cartoon-like drawings
on the board and pieces.

BRUCE FORCE
LOST IN OUTER SPACE
BOARD GAME FOR 2 TO 4 PLAYERS

● In this envelope is a Complete and exciting
game of Outer Space. Everything you need for
the thrilling play of this game is here—a colorful board showing the dangers of Outer Space
exploration—playing cards with instructions for
moving on the board and a spinner. Hours of fun
and excitement . . . all inside this one envelope.

IDEAL

☿ BRUCE FORCE — LOST IN OUTER SPACE $50.00
Ideal, 1963
Another one of Ideal's "envelope games." In this one, hero
Bruce Force appears to be doing some oral surgery on an
unwilling patient.

FLASH GORDON TARGET GAME $125.00
1952
Tin target board had a different game on each side.

4000 A.D. INTERSTELLAR CONFLICT GAME $15.00
House Of Games, 1972

APOLLO: A VOYAGE TO THE MOON $15.00
Tracianne, 1969
Moon rocks were included in this game (simulations of course!).

BATTLESTAR GALACTICA $14.00
Parker Brothers, 1978

BLAST OFF $70.00
Selchow & Righter, 1953
Players traveled in their "rockette ships" to distant planets to pick up cargoes of rare minerals.

BLAST-OFF! $40.00
Waddington, 1969
Game contained a small space capsule.

☖ CAPTAIN VIDEO $125.00
Milton Bradley, 1952
Designer: Jim O'Connor

COUNTDOWN $40.00
Lowe, 1967
Designer: Julie Cooper

☖ COUNTDOWN $40.00
Transogram, 1960

☖ FLASH GORDON $75.00
Game Gems/T. Cohn, 1965

FLASH GORDON $15.00
House Of Games, 1977

LOST IN SPACE $55.00
Milton Bradley, 1965
Designer: Jim Houlihan
The Space Family Robinson just can't seem to get away from that one-eyed bastard.

LOST IN SPACE 3-D GAME $225.00
Remco, 1966
This three level cardboard game also came with large spacemen playing pieces.

LUNAR LANDING $20.00
Lays, 1969

MAGNETIC FLYING SAUCERS $30.00
Pressman, 1951

MAJOR MATT MASON SPACE EXPLORATION $67.00
Mattel, 1967
Matt Mason was Mattel's space version of G.I. Joe. Here, players searched for signs of life across a moon landscape that included a spinning volcano.

MELVIN THE MOON MAN $85.00
Remco, 1959

MEN INTO SPACE $75.00
Milton Bradley, 1960
A second version of this game was released when Bill Lundigan, the star of the TV show on which this game was based, wanted the cover to look more like him. The first version showing the astronaut with blond hair (top) is valued at $65.00.

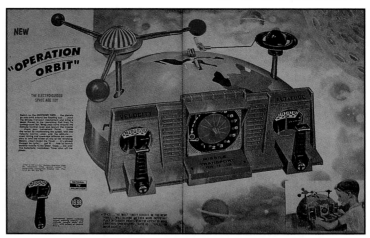

MISSION SPACE GAME $12.00
Samsonite, 1970

𐤀 MOON BLAST OFF $17.00
Schaper, 1970
Designer: Marvin Glass & Assoc.

MOON FLIGHT $12.00
Avon, 1970

MOON SHOT $30.00
Cadaco, 1967

MOON TAG $75.00
Parker Brothers, 1957

ORBITING SPACEWAY $40.00
Kenner, 1970

𐤀 OPERATION ORBIT $110.00
Transogram, 1962

𐤀 ORBIT $40.00
Parker Brothers, 1959

REX MARS SPACE TARGET GAME $100.00
Marx, 1950s
Tin litho target game had plastic spacemen on a horizontal bar that would spin around when hit by ammo from the supplied plastic rifle.

ROCKET PATROL MAGNETIC TARGET GAME $75.00
American Toy, 1950s

ROCKET RACE TO SATURN $35.00
Lido, 1950

ROCKET SATELLITE ACTION GAME $65.00
Tarco, 1950s

ROCKETS AWAY SPACE TRAVEL GAME $55.00
Amsco, 1952

SIREN SPARKLE SPACE TARGET $125.00
Knickerbocker, 1950s
When the spaceship was hit with the dart-loaded Super Atomic Pistol, it spun and sparkled as a siren blared.

𐤀 SPACE 1999 $16.00
Milton Bradley, 1975

SPACE AGE GAME	$75.00
Parker Brothers, 1953	
SPACE CHASE	$30.00
United Nations Constructors, 1967	
SPACE GAME	$50.00
Parker Brothers, 1953	
SPACE LINES 3-D GAME	$15.00
Invicto, 1969	
☊ SPACE PILOT	$70.00
Cadaco, 1951	
SPACE PILOT	$30.00
Citation, 1963	
SPACE RACE	$35.00
Built-Rite, 1960s	
SPACE RACE	$5.00
Ed-U-Cards, 1969	
STAR TREK	$45.00
Hasbro, 1974	

Based on the NBC cartoon that used the original cast's voices.

STAR TREK	$75.00
Ideal, 1967	
Designer: Julie Cooper	
☊ STAR TREK MARBLE MAZE GAME	$80.00
Hasbro, 1967	

☊ STEVE SCOTT SPACE SCOUT $80.00
Transogram, 1952
This space hero was named after the Transogram president's grandson.

☊ SUPER TARGET DART GAME $130.00
Superior/T. Cohn, 1950s

TONY THE TIGER ASTRONAUT SPACE GAME $30.00
Kelloggs, 1960s

DISNEY'S WORLD

While most Disney games are relatively inexpensive, other Disney memorabilia, namely animation cels, is running into the thousands of dollars. There also seems to be a renewed and growing interest in Disneyland, and the games based on the park itself. When Walt Disney created his little mouse back in the 30s, he couldn't have imagined the impact his characters would have on generations of kids... and collectors!

20,000 LEAGUES UNDER THE SEA $60.00
Gardner, 1960s

20,000 LEAGUES UNDER THE SEA $80.00
Jacmar, 1954

20,000 LEAGUES UNDER THE SEA $20.00
Lakeside, 1975

♟ ADVENTURELAND $28.00
Parker Brothers, 1956
Artwork: Lou Green
There were games available based on every "land" in the park. They were sold in stores and throughout Disneyland for $1.00 each.

ANNETTE'S SECRET PASSAGE GAME $35.00
Parker Brothers, 1958

BABES IN TOYLAND $20.00
Whitman, 1961
Designer: Reuben Klamer

♟ BABES IN TOYLAND $32.00
Parker Brothers, 1961
Artwork: Lou Green

BAMBI CARD GAME $8.00
Russell, 1946

CINDERELLA $8.00
Cadaco, 1975

♟ CINDERELLA $40.00
Parker Brothers, 1964
Artwork: Lou Green
The playing pieces were supposedly Cinderella's lost slipper, but thrifty Parker Brothers simply painted the Monopoly "shoe" playing piece and called it a glass slipper.

CINDERELLA CARD GAME $13.00
Transogram, 1965

DAVY CROCKETT ADVENTURE GAME $55.00
Gardner, 1956
Game featured colorful cards showing "Davy Goes to Congress," "Davy at the Alamo," and others.

DAVY CROCKETT CARD GAME $25.00
Ed-U-Cards, 1955

♟ DAVY CROCKETT FRONTIERLAND $55.00
Parker Brothers, 1955
Artwork: Lou Green

DAVY CROCKETT INDIAN SCOUTING GAME $80.00
Whitman, 1955

DAVY CROCKETT RADAR ACTION GAME $80.00
Ewing, 1955
The radar in this case was a magnet underneath the game board that was used to steer playing pieces along.

᛭ DAVY CROCKETT RESCUE RACE $60.00
Gabriel, 1955

DAVY CROCKETT TARGET GAME $50.00
1954
Metal litho target had an Indian scene at the bottom and Davy's picture at the top.

DAVY CROCKETT, ADVENTURES OF $65.00
Harett-Gilmar, 1955

DISNEY SCORE AROUND GAME $30.00
Ideal, 1964

᛭ DISNEYLAND $40.00
Transogram, 1955
Some of the artwork for this game was done before the park even opened. Consequently, a few rides and attractions rendered by the game's artist never materialized in the park, for instance, Transogram's vision of Tomorrowland. This was released with a new cover in 1960 showing Mickey and Donald leading a group of kids through the Sleeping Beauty Castle. It's valued at $40.00 as well.

᛭ DISNEYLAND $45.00
Whitman, 1965

DISNEYLAND DONALD DUCK CARD GAME $10.00
Whitman, 1956

DISNEYLAND EXPRESS $40.00
Russell, 1955
Box contained a tray shaped like a train which held card games of Snow White, Donald Duck, Pinocchio, Mickey Mouse, Bambi, and the 3 Little Pigs.

DISNEYLAND FUN BOX $35.00
Whitman, 1965

DISNEYLAND GAME — A WORLD IN ITSELF $500.00
Rand-McNally, 1950s
Artwork: Bruce Bushman

DISNEYLAND MONORAIL CARD GAMES $55.00
Russell, 1960
Box contained a tray shaped like the Monorail which held card games of Snow White, Donald Duck, Pinocchio, Mickey Mouse, Bambi, and the 3 Little Pigs.

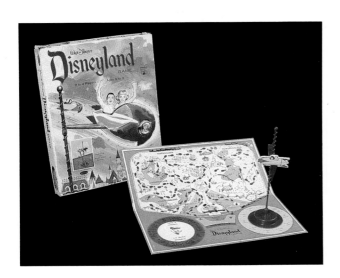

DONALD DUCK $30.00
Whitman, 1949

DONALD DUCK BIG GAME BOX $15.00
Whitman, 1979

DONALD DUCK CARD GAME $11.00
Russell, 1946

DONALD DUCK CARD GAME $15.00
Transogram, 1966

DONALD DUCK RING TOSS $25.00
Transogram, 1961
This was a 14" stand-up masonite cut-out of Donald.
His nephews would appear when rings would hook on his
target arm. A smaller version without the moving arms
was also available, valued at $20.00.

DONALD DUCK'S PARTY GAME $30.00
Parker Brothers, 1950s

ELECTRIC DISNEYLAND TOURS QUIZ $50.00
Jacmar, 1956

⚲ FANTASYLAND $35.00
Parker Brothers, 1956
Artwork: Lou Green

⚲ FRONTIERLAND $30.00
Parker Brothers, 1956
Artwork: Lou Green

GOOFY FINDS HIS MARBLES GAME $20.00
Whitman, 1970s
Designer: Reuben Klamer

GOOFY'S MAD MAZE $15.00
Whitman, 1970

GORDO AND PEPITO $90.00
Milton Bradley, 1947

HAUNTED MANSION $30.00
Lakeside, 1970s

IT'S A SMALL WORLD $13.00
Parker Brothers, 1965

⚲ HARDY BOYS TREASURE GAME $50.00
Parker Brothers, 1957
Artwork: Lou Green

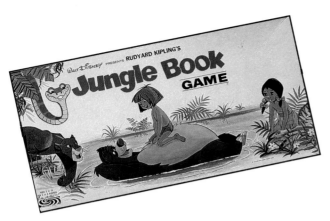

⚬ JUNGLE BOOK $15.00
Parker Brothers, 1966
Artwork: Lou Green

JUNGLE BOOK CARD GAME $10.00
Ed-U-Cards, 1966

LUDWIG VON DRAKE CANNONEERS $40.00
Transogram, 1962
When center of target is hit, plastic figures of Huey and
Dewey come shooting out of a cannon which is pictured
on the target.

LUDWIG VON DRAKE CARD GAME $10.00
Laff 'n Learn, 1960

LUDWIG VON DRAKE RING TOSS $20.00
Transogram, 1962
Set came with a 18" tall figure of Ludwig.

LUDWIG VON DRAKE SCORE-A-MATIC
    BALL TOSS $50.00
Transogram, 1962
When you tossed a ball into Ludwig's hat on this 20"
high target, his eyes would wiggle and the score-a-matic
would register. The ball would be returned to you through
a chute in the front.

LUDWIG VON DRAKE TIDDLEY WINKS $15.00
Whitman, 1962

LUDWIG VON DRAKE WIGGLE-WAGGLE GAME $30.00
Transogram, 1962

MARY POPPINS $35.00
Milton Bradley, 1964
Race from Cherry Tree Lane to the Park. This came with
a magic whirl spinner with Mary on one side and Bert on
the other.

MARY POPPINS $35.00
Whitman, 1964

MARY POPPINS CARD GAME $13.00
Russell, 1964

⚬ MARY POPPINS CAROUSEL GAME $30.00
Parker Brothers, 1964
Artwork: Lou Green

MICKEY MOUSE $12.00
Parker Brothers, 1976

MICKEY MOUSE $45.00
Jacmar, 1950

MICKEY MOUSE CANASTA JR. $30.00
Russell, 1950

⚬ MICKEY MOUSE CLUB GAME IN DISNEYLAND $55.00
Whitman, 1956

MICKEY MOUSE CLUB RUMMY	$17.00
Transogram, 1966	
MICKEY MOUSE CLUB TIDDLEY WINKS	$8.00
Whitman, 1963	
MICKEY MOUSE ELECTRIC TREASURE HUNT	$60.00
Tudor, 1960	
MICKEY MOUSE GAME BOX	$55.00
Parker Brothers, 1953	

MICKEY MOUSE JR. ROYAL RUMMY	$7.00
Whitman, 1970s	
MICKEY MOUSE LOTTO	$15.00
Jaymar, 1950	
MICKEY MOUSE POP-UP GAME	$15.00
Whitman, 1970s	
MICKEY MOUSE STAND-UP LOTTO	$25.00
Gabriel, 1956	

MICKEY MOUSE TOP HAT TARGET GAME $45.00
Transogram, 1963
When the center of the target was hit, plastic ducks came flying out right at you from inside a top hat on the target.

♟ **MONORAIL GAME** $45.00
Parker Brothers, 1960
Artwork: Lou Green
A second version was released in 1966. It's not as attractive and valued at $18.00.

MOUSEKETEER GAME $48.00
Parker Brothers, 1963
Artwork: Lou Green

MY FIRST GAME $18.00
Gabriel, 1955

ONE HUNDRED AND ONE DALMATIONS $30.00
Whitman, 1960

PETER PAN $20.00
Hunt Wesson, 1969

♟ **PETER PAN** $33.00
Transogram, 1953
There were two different covers produced. One was red, the other, blue.

PINOCCHIO $20.00
Whitman, 1962

PINOCCHIO	$18.00	SLEEPING BEAUTY	$38.00

PINOCCHIO $18.00
Parker Brothers, 1971

PINOCCHIO CARD GAME $10.00
Russell, 1946

& PIRATES OF THE CARIBBEAN $15.00
Parker Brothers, 1967
Artwork: Lou Green

& RIVERBOAT $35.00
Parker Brothers, 1960
Artwork: Lou Green
As in the case of the Monorail game, a second version was released in 1966. It's not as attractive and valued at $15.00.

ROBIN HOOD $20.00
Parker Brothers, 1973

SLEEPING BEAUTY $38.00
Whitman, 1958

SLEEPING BEAUTY $47.00
Parker Brothers, 1952
Artwork: Lou Green

SNOW WHITE AND THE SEVEN DWARFS $10.00
Parker Brothers, 1970s

SNOW WHITE AND THE SEVEN DWARFS
   CARD GAME $12.00
Russell, 1946

STEPS AND CHUTES $24.00
Transogram, 1963
Chutes and Ladders with the Disney clan.

♟ SWAMP FOX $45.00
Parker Brothers, 1960
Artwork: Lou Green
This game was based on a recurring character—Francis Marion, a Revolutionary War hero—from the "Disneyland" television show. Leslie Nielsen's character was known as the Swamp Fox.

SWORD IN THE STONE $25.00
Parker Brothers, 1963
Artwork: Lou Green

THREE LITTLE PIGS CARD GAME $14.00
Russell, 1946

♟ TOMORROWLAND $40.00
Parker Brothers, 1956
Artwork: Lou Green

WALT DISNEY PICTURE DOMINOES $22.00
Transogram, 1955
These cardboard dominoes featured Mickey, Donald, Pluto, Pinocchio, Bambi, Dumbo, and Dopey.

WALT DISNEY WORLD $18.00
Milton Bradley, 1974
Designer: Doug Beck

WALT DISNEY'S UNCLE REMUS GAME $85.00
Parker Brothers, 1940s

♟ WALT DISNEY'S WONDERFUL WORLD
     OF COLOR GAME $50.00
Whitman, 1961

♟ WINNIE THE POOH HONEY TREE GAME $30.00
Ideal, 1966
Object was to help Winnie get down by dropping a marble through the tree, but sometimes a pesky bee would force the player to move back.

♟ Wizzer Wheel $25.00
Ideal, 1964

♟ Zorro $42.00
Whitman, 1959

♟ Zorro $48.00
Parker Brothers, 1966
Artwork: Lou Green

Zorro Beanbag-Darts $65.00
Gardner, 1960

Zorro Magic Slate Game $50.00
Strathmore, 1960

Zorro Target Game $80.00
Knickerbocker, 1959

Zorro Target Game $180.00
Superior/T. Cohn, 1960

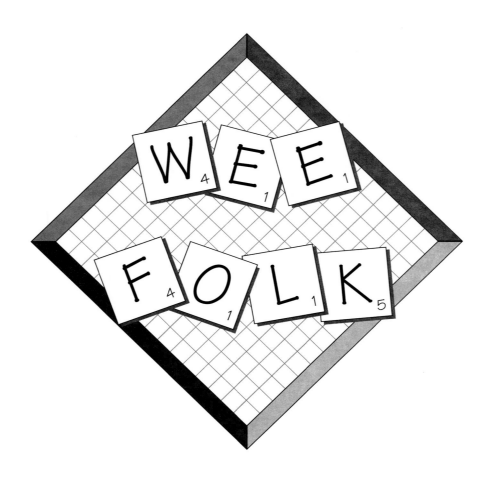

Although these games aren't the most collectible, they did serve their purpose for children. As one brochure, included in an old game exclaimed, "Why games? To challenge — To compete — To merit reward — To lose graciously. These are the thrills of playing games which have attracted children and adults alike down through the ages." Lose graciously? Yeah, right. Now, hurry up and spin, before I smash this board over your head!

4 LITTLE PIGS $14.00
Ideal, 1961
Kids tried to build 3-D houses from pieces in the center of the gameboard.

A DAY WITH ZIGGY $15.00
Milton Bradley, 1977

⅄ AIRPLANE GAME $12.00
Hasbro, 1966

ALLIGAROO $20.00
Transogram, 1964
A mix 'n match animal game for kids.

ALPHABET GAME $7.00
Selchow & Righter, 1972
Players went around the board picking up three-dimensional letters to complete simple words.

ANIMAL FUN GAME $10.00
Milton Bradley, 1953

ANIMAL LAND $5.00
Selchow & Righter, 1974

ANIMAL TALK $25.00
Mattel, 1964
This game came with a barn that played 12 different animal sounds.

⅄ ANIMAL TWISTER $18.00
Milton Bradley, 1967
Designer: Chuck Foley
A kiddie variation of Bradley's hit game, Twister.

ARABIAN KNIGHTS FLYING CARPET GAME $13.00
Selchow & Righter, 1972

BABAR $15.00
Milton Bradley, 1968

⅄ BABAR AND HIS FRIENDS SEE-SAW GAME $22.00
Milton Bradley, 1961
Designer: Jim O'Connor

⅄ BANDERSNATCH $15.00
Mattel, 1968

BEARS AND BEES $8.00
Transogram, 1962

BIG FOOT $10.00
Milton Bradley, 1977

BIRD BRAIN $18.00
Milton Bradley, 1966
Designer: Reuben Klamer

BIRTHDAY CAKE $8.00
Transogram, 1962

BLACK BALL EXPRESS $10.00
Schaper, 1957

BLACK BEAUTY $35.00
Transogram, 1958
This was based on the famous children's classic.

BLACK CAT $10.00
Creative Playthings, 1973

⚉ BLOW FOOTBALL $17.00
Hayter, 1966

⚉ BOBBSEY TWINS $20.00
Milton Bradley, 1957
Designer: Jim O'Connor
Flossie, Freddie, Nan, and Bert visit Meadow Brook Farm where they pick their way through a vegetable garden avoiding insects without the use of pesticides. Turnips and onions were the only vegetables that set you back.

BUG HOUSE $18.00
Lakeside, 1964

BUG-A-BOO $13.00
Whitman, 1968
Game contained two spinning metal bugs that would head for color coded holes in the plastic gameboard.

BULLDOG $6.00
Selchow & Righter, 1974

BUNNY HO $20.00
Saalfield, 1954
This "3 in 1 Game" contained the games Bunny Ho, Storm the Castle, and Splash.

⚉ BUNNY RABBIT GAME $35.00
Parker Brothers, 1961
Artwork: Lou Green

BUTTERFLIES $12.00

Cadaco, 1967

Youngsters moved plastic butterflies over a board, passing from one flower to the next.

BUZZ $6.00

Selchow & Righter, 1955

♟ **CAMP GRANADA** $33.00

Milton Bradley, 1965

Designer: Reuben Klamer

Allen Sherman's hit song was the inspiration for this game invented by Klamer and Sherman's teenage son. The TV commercial featured the chubby singer bad-mouthing his own game to entice kids into getting their parents to buy it.

CANDY CAPERS $12.00

Transogram, 1968

Players tried to fill their empty candy boxes by collecting plastic, chocolate pieces.

♟ **CANDYLAND** $30.00

Milton Bradley, 1955

Designer: Eleanor Abbott

Invented by Miss Abbott who, while recuperating from polio, enjoyed creating amusing pastimes for children with the same affliction. She designed the game to be very simple—matching colors and objects—so that children who couldn't read could understand it.

CAPTAIN KIDD $40.00

Lowell, 1950s

CARS N' TRUCKS $18.00

Ideal, 1961

Kids tried to build 3-D cars and trucks from pieces in the center of the gameboard.

♟ **CAT AND MOUSE** $15.00

Parker Brothers, 1964

Artwork: Jack McMann

This is Parker artist, McMann's favorite cover.

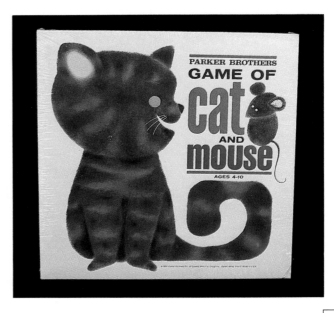

CAT IN THE BAG $10.00
Schaper, 1974
Players took turns carefully lifting the claws that kept a
plastic cat in a bag. When somebody lifted one too many,
the spring-loaded feline would pop out.

CATCH A CROOK $14.00
Ideal, 1971
Designers: Eddy Goldfarb, Rene Soriano

CHARLEY 'N ME ROBOT GAME $40.00
Topper, 1967

CHERRY PIE FUN GAME $12.00
Transogram, 1966
Designer: Reuben Klamer
Try to place your marbles on the tricky rotating pie.

CHICKEN LOTTO $15.00
Ideal, 1966
Designer: Eddy Goldfarb
Colored marbles would pop out of a chicken when you
pushed his tail. These were used to fill the spaces on your
card in this pre-school version of Bingo.

CHICKEN OUT $13.00
Milton Bradley, 1966
Designer: Marvin Glass & Assoc.

CHICKEN, THE GAME OF $10.00
Schaper, 1957

⚇ CHICLETS GUM VILLAGE GAME $20.00
Hasbro, 1959
First one who made it to the Chiclets Gum Factory won a
small box of Chiclets, which were supplied in
every game.

⚇ CHILDREN'S HOUR $15.00
Parker Brothers, 1961
Parker's set contained three games that
each took around twenty minutes to play —
hence the title.

⚇ CHOO CHOO CHARLIE GAME $40.00
Milton Bradley, 1969
This game was based on the mascot for
Good n' Plenty candy.

CHOO CHOO: THE TRAIN GAME $20.00
Transogram, 1963

⚆ CHUTES AND LADDERS $20.00
Milton Bradley, 1956
Based on an English game, "Snakes and Ladders," good deeds sent children up ladders; when they disobeyed, it was down the chutes. The 1943 version is valued at $30.00.

CLICKETY-CLAK $18.00
Milton Bradley, 1953

CLIMB THE MOUNTAIN $20.00
Parker Brothers, 1951

CLOWN CAPERS $10.00
Whitman, 1960

CLOWN CHECKERS $7.00
Whitman, 1960s
Designer: Eddy Goldfarb

COBBLER AND THE ELVES, THE $30.00
Hasbro, 1964

CONFETTI THE CLOWN $13.00
Cadaco, 1968

⚆ COOTIE $15.00
Schaper, 1949
Designer: W.H. Schaper
Start with the body, then add the head. First one to assemble the multicolored plastic "cootie" won the game. This was an old game originally played on paper and created around WWI.

COOTIE HOUSE $32.00
Schaper, 1966

COOTIE, DELUXE 6 $23.00
Schaper, 1950s
The deluxe edition contained six cooties instead of four and came in a larger box.

COOTIE, GIANT $80.00
Schaper, 1950s
This played like the regular Cootie, but on a larger scale. Also, the bodies of the Cooties had a slot in the top and a door on the bottom so they could be used as banks.

CRACKER JACK GAME $18.00

Milton Bradley, 1976

Collectible in that the game was filled with the little
prizes that the snack is so famous for.

CROSS OVER THE BRIDGE $10.00

Kohner, 1970

DANCING PRINCESS, THE $30.00

Hasbro, 1964

🎎 DOLLY AND DANIEL WHALE $40.00

Milton Bradley, 1964

DON'T GO OVERBOARD $8.00

Schaper, 1971

Try to get all of your magnetized sailors on board the
ship without being repelled overboard by others.

DONKEY PARTY GAME $8.00

Saalfield, 1950

🎎 DOUBLE OR NOTHIN' $20.00

Remco, 1958

DOWN ON THE FARM $12.00

Hasbro, 1966

🎎 DUNCE $13.00

Schaper, 1955

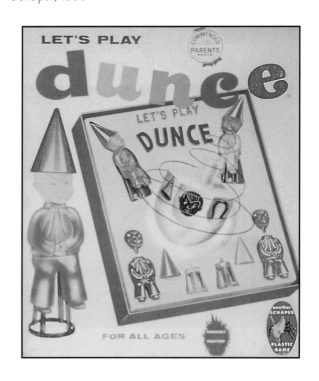

a cute little folks animal game

EGG HEADS $8.00
Transogram, 1962

ELLSWORTH ELEPHANT $48.00
Selchow & Righter, 1960

ELSIE AND HER FAMILY $45.00
Selchow & Righter, 1941
Object of the game was to get Elsie and her
family in their stalls.

EMMET KELLY'S CIRCUS GAME $50.00
All-Fair, 1953

FAIRY TALE GAME $15.00
Selchow & Righter, 1962
Each player experienced the adventures of such
characters as Puss in Boots and the Ugly Duck-
ling. Just what the kid with the inferiority complex needs.

↟ FEED THE ELEPHANT $28.00
Cadaco, 1952

↟ FIREHOUSE MOUSE $33.00
Transogram, 1967

FLEEP HOUSE $8.00
Parker Brothers, 1971
Game came with a plastic house. Kids would
drop a fleep down the chimney, then try to
guess where it was hiding.

↟ FOREST FRIENDS $10.00
Milton Bradley, 1962

GINGERBREAD MAN $20.00
Selchow & Righter, 1961
Kids had to piece together an eight piece puzzle of a gingerbread house to win this game.

GINGERBREAD MAN GAME $14.00
Transogram, 1962

GOLDILOCKS $20.00
Cadaco, 1955

GOLDILOCKS AND THE THREE BEARS $5.00
Cadaco, 1974

GOLDILOCKS AND THE THREE BEARS $6.00
Selchow & Righter, 1973

GUESS 'N BEE $12.00
Schaper, 1964

GULLIVER $15.00
Ravensburg, 1971

HANSEL AND GRETEL $40.00
Lowell, 1963
A wheel in the center of the board would move, changing the path you were on and sending players in different directions.

HAPPY BIRTHDAY GAME PARTY PAK $5.00
Cadaco, 1974
Here was an instant birthday party — just add the kids. Came with rules and equipment for dozens of games.

♟ HAPPY FACE $15.00
Milton Bradley, 1968
Designer: Jim Houlihan

HAPPY HAPPY BIRTHDAY $18.00
Mattel, 1964
Game board was a plastic birthday cake that played "Happy Birthday" at the turn of a crank.

♟ HAPPY LITTLE TRAIN $15.00
Milton Bradley, 1957
Designer: Jim O'Connor

♟ HEY PA, THERE'S A GOAT ON THE ROOF $30.00
Parker Brothers, 1965
Artwork: Jack McMann
Looking for a 3-D game to compete with others on the market, Parker Brothers fell in love with this unusual game title. Unfortunately, kids didn't, and the game was an absolute bomb.

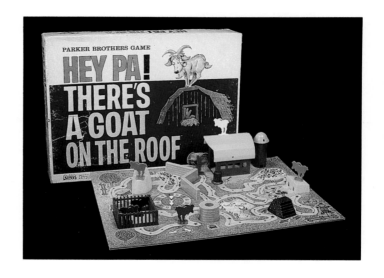

Hi Ho Cherry-O! $10.00
Whitman, 1960

♟ Hi Ho Santa Claus $30.00
Whitman, 1962

♟ Hickety Pickety $20.00
Parker Brothers, 1954

Hide & Seek $22.00
Ideal, 1967

♟ Hide 'N Thief $15.00
Whitman, 1965
Designer: Reuben Klamer

Hillbillies Comin' Round the Mountain $15.00
Hasbro, 1964

Hillbillies Feudin' Time $15.00
Hasbro, 1964

Hillbillies Hoedown $15.00
Hasbro, 1964

Hippity Hop $50.00
Corey, 1947

Hippopotamus Electronic Puzzle Game $20.00
Remco, 1961
A version of Fascination for the very young.

♟ Hocus Pocus $65.00
Transogram, 1968
Who will be the first to collect ten magic rings and make
the rabbits pop out of the hat?

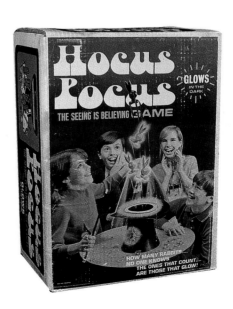

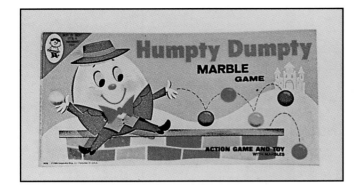

HOMESTRETCH $15.00
Milton Bradley, 1974

HOPSKIP AND JUMP $7.00
Selchow & Righter, 1965
Contained four large squeeze-toy playing pieces — a fish, duck, turtle, and frog.

HOP•POP $15.00
Schaper, 1968
Designer: Marvin Glass

HOT DIGGITY DOG $20.00
Transogram, 1967
Set at an amusement park, a crank of the plastic hot dog machine would determine your moves.

HOT NUMBERS $5.00
Selchow & Righter, 1948

HUFF 'N PUFF $17.00
Schaper, 1968
A spring loaded wolf would pop up to smash players "pig houses."

HUMPTY DUMPTY $50.00
Lowell, 1960
Designer: Julie Cooper
Artwork: Wally Wood

☖ HUMPTY DUMPTY
MARBLE GAME $10.00
Hasbro, 1966

IT...GAME OF TAG $25.00
Gabriel, 1956

JACK AND JILL $12.00
Schaper, 1976

☖ JACK AND JILL JACKS GAME $10.00
Hasbro, 1966

☖ JACK AND THE BEANSTALK $40.00
National Games, 1941

☖ JACK AND THE BEANSTALK $22.00
Transogram, 1957

JACK BE NIMBLE $10.00
Schaper, 1974
Designer: Marvin Glass & Assoc.
Kids tried to get Jumpin' Jack to soar high enough to clear the flame. Great balls o' fire!

JACK THE GIANT KILLER $40.00
Lowell, 1950s

JEEPERS CREEPERS $15.00
1950
This game had a battery-operated board that shook cardboard "bugs" down a racecourse toward the finish line.

JINGLE DINGLE'S
    WEATHER GAME $30.00
Lowell, 1954
This game was based on that ever-interesting subject — the weather. Using a 3-D weather station, players tried to clear their states of hazardous weather conditions.

♟ JOHNNY ON THE PONY $32.00
Remco, 1959

JUNIOR BINGO-MATIC $10.00
Transogram, 1968

♟ KING OF THE CHEESE $30.00
Milton Bradley, 1959

♟ KING OF THE HILL $15.00
Schaper, 1964
Designer: Marvin Glass & Assoc.
Your marbles race to climb the hill but watch out for traps or you'll wind up at the bottom.

KOO KOO CHOO CHOO! $28.00
Ohio Art, 1967
Designer: Marvin Glass & Assoc.

KOOKIE CHICKS $15.00
Milton Bradley, 1964
Kids maneuvered plastic chickens with a magnetic wand.

♟ LET'S FACE IT $50.00
Hasbro, 1955

♟ LI'L STINKER $12.00
Schaper, 1956

167

LITTLE BENNY $10.00
Selchow & Righter, 1957
Mom, Pop, and Little Benny Beaver had to traverse the
stepping stones in the river to get to the Beaver's winter home in this game.

♟ LITTLE BLACK SAMBO $100.00
Cadaco, 1951
The first one to get home to the pancakes won the
game.

LITTLE BOY BLUE $18.00
Cadaco, 1955

♟ LITTLE NODDY'S TAXI GAME $90.00
Parker Brothers, 1956
This game was based on a series of children's books that,
incidentally, were banned in certain regions of England
because conservatives thought the relationship between
some of the characters could be construed as homosexual.

LITTLE PRINCE $8.00
Cadaco, 1974

♟ LITTLE RASCALS CLUBHOUSE BINGO $45.00
Gabriel, 1955

LITTLE RED HEN $14.00
1950
Players followed the path of the Little Red Hen. The first
to reach the table with bread won.

LOLI POP LANE $15.00
Hasbro, 1964

LUNCH BUNCH EASY ON THE KETCHUP $6.00
Lakeside, 1975

MAGIC MIDWAY $30.00
Cadaco, 1962

MAGIC, MAGIC, MAGIC GAME $30.00
Remco, 1975

MARBLE RACEWAY $15.00
Amsco, 1964
Line up marbles on the plastic tower and watch them
pass on curves, collide, and race for the lead position.

McDONALD'S FARM $33.00
Selchow & Righter, 1948
Kiddie game set at the county fair. The 1965 version
with a different cover is valued at $12.00.

McDONALD'S GAME $20.00
Milton Bradley, 1975

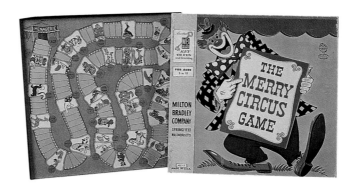

♟ MERRY CIRCUS GAME $12.00
Milton Bradley, 1960
Designer: Jim O'Connor

MERRY-GO-ROUND $35.00
Cadaco, 1951
Get three children on horses and you win! Lots
of fun just in the assembly of the game.

♟ MERRY-GO-ROUND $15.00
Whitman, 1965

MIXIES $15.00
Ed-U-Cards, 1965

MONKEY TREE $8.00
Transogram, 1962

MONKEYS AND COCONUTS $20.00
Schaper, 1965
Designer: Marvin Glass & Assoc.

MOTHER GOOSE $6.00
Cadaco, 1974

MOTHER GOOSE $20.00
Lowe, 1941

♟ MR. BUG GOES TO TOWN $38.00
Milton Bradley, 1955
Designer: Jim O'Connor

♟ MR. DOODLE'S DOG $35.00
Selchow & Righter, 1948
Designer: Howard Garis
In their catalog, Selchow & Righter's selling
point of this item was, "It's the only dog game
on the market." Designed by the creator of
Uncle Wiggily.

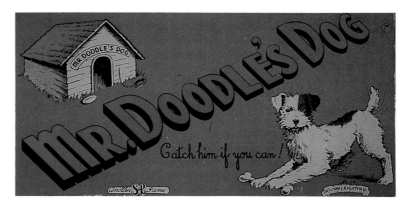

♟ MR. MACHINE GAME $75.00
Ideal, 1961
Artwork: Ralph Pereida
Get Mr. Machine to his factory while avoiding hazards en route. This came with a plastic Mr. Machine move indicator.

MR. MAD $25.00
Ideal, 1970
Designer: Marvin Glass & Assoc.

MR. REMBRANDT $25.00
Ideal, 1970

MUG SHOTS $12.00
Cadaco, 1975

♟ MUSINGO $14.00
Mattel, 1962
The organ grinder played real music and called tunes for each player's move. The first one to get five notes in a row won.

♟ NOAH'S ARK $14.00
Cadaco, 1961

NUMBERLAND COUNTING GAME $6.00
Selchow & Righter, 1972

OLD MAID $9.00
Built-Rite, 1964

PERILS OF PAULINE $45.00
Marx, 1964

PETER RABBIT $67.00
Gabriel, 1946

PETER RABBIT $28.00
Milton Bradley, 1948

PICKIN' $7.00
Schaper, 1955

PIG IN THE GARDEN $12.00
Schaper, 1964
First player to fill his garden with vegetables won this game.

PIGS IN A POKE $8.00
Transogram, 1962

☖ PINHEAD $25.00
Remco, 1959

☖ PINOCCHIO $15.00
Transogram, 1970

PIRATE'S COVE $33.00
Gabriel, 1956
Captain Kidd and Long John hunt for buried treasure.

PLAY IT COOL $20.00
Lakeside, 1962
When a green light lit up on the board everybody scrambled to leap-frog two penguins up a three-dimensional ice field using only one hand.

POISON IVY $22.00
Ideal, 1969

☖ POP UP STORE $65.00
Milton Bradley, 1949
Designer: Jim O'Connor
This three-dimensional game was a kid's dream. You were left in a toy store and a soda fountain with money to burn.

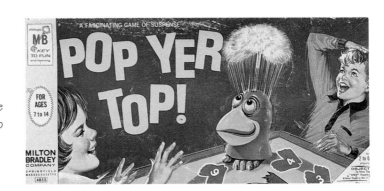

☖ POP YER TOP $20.00
Milton Bradley, 1968

☖ RAGGEDY ANN $24.00
Milton Bradley, 1954
This game had large illustrations of Ann, Andy, and all of their friends.

RED RIDING HOOD $55.00
Lowell, 1963
Artwork: Wally Wood
Get to Granny's house before the magnetic remote-controlled wolf does.

171

👤 REDDY-CLOWN 3 RING CIRCUS $36.00
Parker Brothers, 1952

ROBINSON CRUSOE $45.00
Lowell, 1961
Designer: Julie Cooper
Contained a magnetic moving Crusoe.

ROCK, PAPER, SCISSORS $20.00
Ideal, 1968
Designer: Edward Bodenhamer
Even the most basic of all games was turned into a marketable item in the 60s.

ROPES & LADDERS $12.00
Parker Brothers, 1954

ROPES AND LADDERS $10.00
Whitman, 1957

RUNAWAY ZOO $13.00
Selchow & Righter, 1965
Animals on spinning tops tried to find their way back to their cages.

SANTA CLAUS CARD GAME $15.00
Russell, 1964

SANTA'S WORKSHOP $45.00
Milton Bradley, 1959
Designer: Jim O'Connor

SCARECROW $10.00
Schaper, 1952

SCAT $10.00
Cadaco, 1967

SCOOT $23.00
Transogram, 1955

SCREECH $20.00
Parker Brothers, 1972
Designer: Marvin Glass & Assoc.

SHAKE $6.00
Schaper, 1955

👤 SHMO $45.00
Remco, 1959

SHUTTLE GAME $8.00
Transogram, 1962

SILLY CARNIVAL $12.00
Whitman, 1969

SIMON SAYS $20.00
Cardinal, 1964

👤 SIMPLE SIMON BALLOON GAME $10.00
Hasbro, 1966

SINGING BONE, THE $40.00
Hasbro, 1964

SKEDADDLE: GAME OF
    HURDLES $12.00
Cadaco, 1965

SKILLETS AND CAKES $28.00
Milton Bradley, 1946

SMARTY $8.00
1959
An arithmetic bingo game for kids.

☖ SMOKEY BEAR GAME $35.00
Milton Bradley, 1973
Designer: Doug Beck

SMOKEY THE FOREST FIRE
    PREVENTIN' BEAR $40.00
Ideal, 1961
Youngsters learned the do's and
don'ts of forest safety.

SNARE $6.00
Whitman, 1954

SNOW WHITE AND THE
    SEVEN DWARFS $8.00
Cadaco, 1977

SPIDER AND FLY $8.00
Whitman, 1962

SPIDER'S WEB $12.00
Multiple Plastics, 1969

☖ SPRING CHICKEN $20.00
Mattel, 1968

SQUIRT $23.00
Milton Bradley, 1955
This game was about a whale.

STEPS TO TOYLAND $37.00
Parker Brothers, 1955
As each player moved up the steps
to Toyland he was rewarded with different toys. The playing pieces were
small plaster children.

SUGAR BOWL $35.00
Transogram, 1950
This is not based on the famous New
Year's day football game. Sugar Bowl
is set at an ice cream fountain.

SWOOP $8.00
Whitman, 1969

TALLY HO! $10.00
Whitman, 1961

☖ TERRY TELL TIME GAME $18.00
Transogram, 1950s

THING DING ROBOT
    GAME $127.00
Schaper, 1966

THREE BLIND MICE $8.00
Lakeside, 1967
Game came in a small plastic box that resembled a wedge of cheese.

THREE LITTLE PIGS $10.00
Ed-U-Cards, 1956
Designer: Julie Cooper

THREE LITTLE PIGS $8.00
Selchow & Righter, 1959

♟ TICKLE BEE $20.00
Schaper, 1959
Kids would guide the magnetic bee through a maze using a magnetic wand to try to get it back to the hive.

♟ TICKY THE CLOWN CLOCK GAME $6.00
Happy Hour, 1956

TING-A-LING BINGO $6.00
Cadaco, 1974
Instead of numbers, this game had kids matching symbols from major holidays to win.

TOOT! TOOT! $15.00
Selchow & Righter, 1964
Children moved their wooden trains along a large railroad game board.

♟ TOOTSIE ROLL TRAIN GAME $35.00
Hasbro, 1964

TOTEM $23.00
Transogram, 1962
Each player tried to complete a plastic totem pole by collecting cards that spell out the name of the totem figures.

TOY PARADE $40.00
Jaymar, 1950s

♟ TOY TOWN $50.00
Milton Bradley, 1962
Designer: Ted Starcewski

TRACKS $8.00
Ed-U-Cards, 1956
Designer: Julie Cooper

TUGBOAT $15.00
Parker Brothers, 1974
Designer: M. Glass & Assoc.

TUMBLE BUG $12.00
Schaper, 1966

TUNE-IN TV BINGO $5.00
Selchow & Righter, 1970
Designer: Angelo Longo
Players would call out images on the TV screen (car,
horse, hat, etc.) that matched their bingo cards.

TURTLE $13.00
Schaper, 1962

UNCLE WIGGILY $18.00
Milton Bradley, 1954
In this classic, kids had to get Uncle Wiggily past the fox's
den and through the forest to Doc Possum's office.

UNCLE WIGGILY $6.00
Parker Brothers, 1967
Artwork: Jack McMann

WALK ALONG SESAME STREET $10.00
Milton Bradley, 1975
Designer: Doug Beck

WHAT'S COOKING $12.00
Whitman, 1967
Designer: Reuben Klamer
Make a balanced meal in your plastic skillet while keeping
the skillet balanced as well.

⚱ WHERE'S WILLIE? $28.00
Milton Bradley, 1966
This was based on a stunt played on the TV show "Shenani-
gans." It was also one of Milton Bradley's bigger bombs.

WHIRLIGIG $17.00
Milton Bradley, 1963
Designer: Reuben Klamer
A musical chairs game on a board where the last Teddy
Bear to have a seat wins.

WHIRLY BIRD $15.00
Schaper, 1966

⚱ WHO YOU? $10.00
Schaper, 1966
Designer: Marvin Glass & Assoc.

WHOOPS! $15.00
Whitman, 1967
Designer: Reuben Klamer

⚱ WINNER SPINNER $8.00
Whitman, 1953

WINNIE THE POOH $37.00
Parker Brothers, 1954
Artwork: Lou Green

WIZARD OF OZ $15.00
Cadaco, 1974

WUFFLE TREE $7.00
Selchow & Righter, 1955

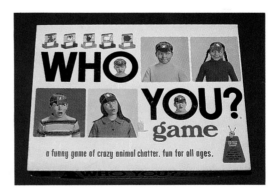

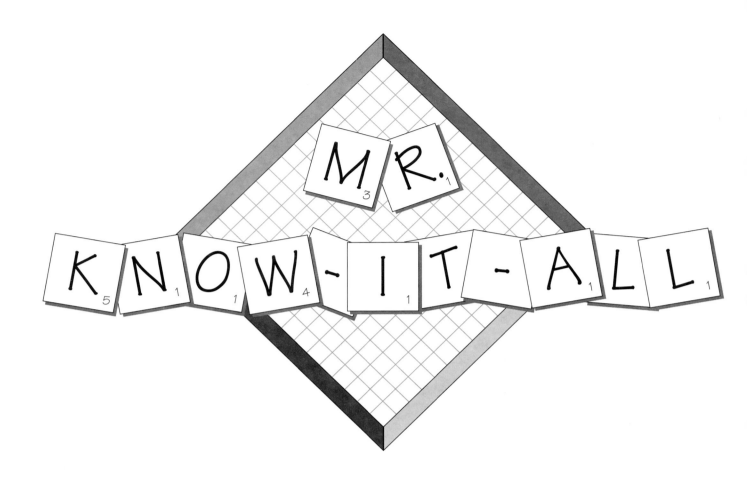

MR. KNOW-IT-ALL

Educational games were that rare breed that tried to meld the worlds of knowledge and fun into one package. Some of these were very imaginative, but unless they had a neat hook, as in Hasbro's Think-A-Tron, kids would usually rather eat their broccoli than play a game that might teach them something. This chapter also includes the many word games that hit the market, especially after Scrabble took the nation by storm.

3 IN-A-ROW BIBLE QUIZ $15.00
Transogram, 1960
Transogram re-issued their large plastic mechanical category selector from their Tic-Tac-Dough game and put new questions in for this item. It also included questions in Spanish.

3 IN-A-ROW HOME QUIZ $15.00
Transogram, 1960

AD-LIB $7.00
Lowe, 1970

& ADDICTION $5.00
Createk, 1968

ADVENTURE IN
  SCIENCE, AN $35.00
Jacmar, 1950
Electric quiz game tested your knowledge on subjects ranging from biology to space.

AFRO-AMERICAN HISTORY
  MYSTERY GAME $10.00
1971
Travel the course of black history by piecing together four historical puzzles and answering questions from fact cards.

ALLEGIANCE $12.00
1964
Youngsters learned about the Constitution in this card game that pictured Lady Liberty on its cover.

AMAZING DR. NIM $12.00
ESR, 1965

ANAGRAMS $5.00
Selchow & Righter, 1949

& ANT FARM GAME $25.00
Uncle Milton, 1969

& AROUND THE WORLD $13.00
Milton Bradley, 1962

AUTHORS $18.00
All-Fair, 1945

BALI $4.00
Selchow & Righter, 1968
Scrabble in card form.

BEAT THE BUZZ $16.00
Kenner, 1958

& BENNY GOODMAN SWINGS INTO A
  GAME OF MUSICAL
  INFORMATION $90.00
Toy Creations, 1940s
The King of Swing had his own music quiz that came complete with a xylophone and questions about popular songs of the day.

BETSY ROSS AND THE
  FLAG $35.00
Transogram, 1961
This was based on one of the titles from Random House's Landmark Book series.

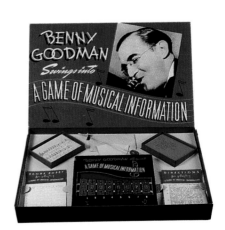

BIBLE ZOO GAME $18.00
Zondervan, 1954

BIRD WATCHER $37.00
Parker Brothers, 1958

BLACK EXPERIENCE, THE $10.00
Theme Productions, 1971
Game traced the progression of black people and their contributions in America from 1619 to 1971.

♟ BLARNEY $13.00
Mattel, 1970

BOGGLE $4.00
Parker Brothers, 1976

BOOK OF KNOWLEDGE ELECTROMATIC
   DIAL QUIZ $23.00
Transogram, 1961
Game had a large plastic dial, dual scorekeepers, and an electromatic stylus. It lit up when a correct answer was selected. Re-named in 1964 as "You Are Right!"

BRAIN WAVES $8.00
Milton Bradley, 1977

CATCHWORD $8.00
Whitman, 1954

CHALLENGE YAHTZEE $5.00
Lowe, 1974

♟ CHIT CHAT $14.00
Milton Bradley, 1963
Designers: Hugh Downs, Sherle Maguire
A game of conversation where points were scored by making statements using word cards and "Lucky Letters."

CLOCK-A-GAME $20.00
Topper, 1966
Players tried to identify faces of U.S. Presidents and animals from around the world among other topics before a large annoying ticker stoped. Interchangeable reels let you play other games as well.

CLOCK-A-WORD $15.00
Topper, 1966
This version had you unscramble letters that appeared and form the longest word in the shortest time.

CROSSWORDS $10.00
Jaymar, 1953

CROSSWORDS $12.00
National Games, 1954

DELUXE SCRABBLE $8.00
Selchow & Righter, 1953
Designer: George Hoehne

♟ DIG $6.00
Parker Brothers, 1959

ELECTRIC CLASSROOM GAME $28.00
Electric Game Co., 1957
Designer: Jim Prentice

Fact Finder Fun	$15.00
Milton Bradley, 1964	
Facts in Five	$10.00
3M, 1967	
Game about the United Nations	$27.00
Payton, 1961	

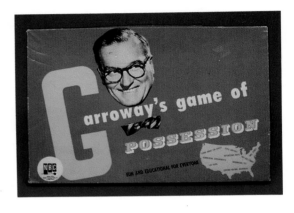

Game about the United States	$12.00
Payton, 1961	
Game of Heroes and Events	$8.00
Selchow & Righter, 1962	
Game of Products and Resources	$7.00
Selchow & Righter, 1962	

S & R released this game to reflect national pride.

Game of State Capitals	$15.00
Parker Brothers, 1952	
Game of States and Cities	$23.00
Parker Brothers, 1947	

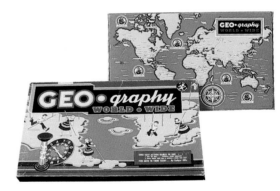

☖ Game of the States	$15.00
Milton Bradley, 1956	
☖ Garroway's Game of Possessions	$40.00
Reco, 1955	
☖ GEO-graphy	$15.00
Cadaco, 1958	

Race against time as you identify cities, oceans, rivers, islands, and seas around the world.

Geography Lotto	$15.00
Milton Bradley, 1956	

☖ Go to the Head of the Class	$14.00
Milton Bradley, 1957	

Designers: Norman Morris, Vincent Coghlan
Two New York City department store employees designed this game to make learning more fun and a family experience.

☖ Going to Jerusalem	$30.00
Parker Brothers, 1955	
Artwork: Amos Gott	

♟ GUESS AGAIN $20.00
Milton Bradley, 1967
This was an electric question and answer game.

♟ HANGMAN $6.00
Milton Bradley, 1976
Designer: Ted Starcewski
Vincent Price is pictured on the cover of this common game.

JOHNNY CAN READ $5.00
Ed-U-Cards, 1956
Designer: Julie Cooper

JOTTO $3.00
Selchow & Righter, 1973

♟ KATE SMITH'S OWN GAME AMERICA $45.00
Toy Creations, 1940s

KEYWORD $15.00
Parker Brothers, 1953
Parker's answer to Scrabble boasted three exclusive features — Color Areas, Key Squares, and Keyword Cards that gave players additional scores.

KNOW THE STARS AND PLANETS $50.00
Milton Bradley, 1960

KNOW YOUR STATES $15.00
Garrad Press, 1955

LET'S GO TO COLLEGE $20.00
Electric Game Co., 1944
Designer: Jim Prentice

LITTLE RED SCHOOL HOUSE $30.00
Parker Brothers, 1952
The questions in this game were graded according to age so everyone could play.

MAGIC ROBOT, THE AMAZING $20.00
Merit, 1953
The idea behind this magnetic question and answer game was used a year later by Pressman for their Groucho's TV Quiz Game and in 1959's Ask the Veda Board.

MEET THE PRESIDENTS $17.00
Selchow & Righter, 1950
This game contained coins with a different president on each.

♟ MEN OF DESTINY $20.00
Milton Bradley, 1956
Designer: Jim O'Connor
Do you know who our 13th President was?

♟ MENTOR $40.00
Hasbro, 1961

♟ MERIT, THE CATHOLIC
    GAME $18.00
Educational Research Corp., 1962
Designer: Edward J. Agnew

MIX 'N SPELL $8.00
Uncle Milton, 1968

♟ MR. BRAIN $35.00
Jacmar, 1959
Children fed their answers into this friendly computer's mouth. His eyes told them if they were right or wrong.

MYSTIC WHEEL OF
    KNOWLEDGE $30.00
Novel Toy, 1950

NUMBLE $9.00
Selchow & Righter, 1968
Scrabble with numbers.

♟ PEEKO $6.00
Watkins-Strathmore, 1964

PERQUACKEY $4.00
Lakeside, 1967
Lakeside's entry into the lettered-dice game.

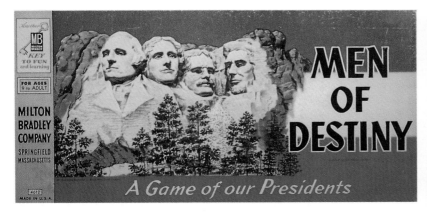

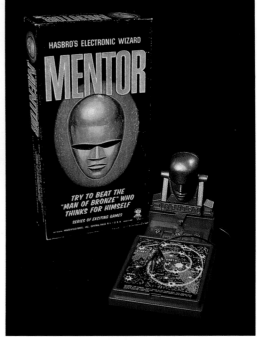

♟ Pirate and Traveler $15.00
Milton Bradley, 1953
Here was educational globe-trotting with the added
thrill of being chased by pirates. This game took youngsters all over the world and taught them about foreign
countries, their cities, products, etc.

Pla-O-Map Game $15.00
Cram, 1968
This Indiana globe company designed their own game
using as the playing board... surprise, a globe!

Play Quiz Game $20.00
Trojan, 1940

Quiz Me $7.00
Milton Bradley, 1950

Quiz Panel $10.00
Cadaco, 1954

Quizmo $5.00
Milton Bradley, 1953
This taught addition and subtraction to youngsters.

♟ Quizziac, The Golden $18.00
Golden Capitol, 1960

♟ Qwik Quiz $25.00
Transogram, 1958

R.S.V.P. $8.00
Selchow & Righter, 1967
This was a three-dimensional crossword game played on
both sides of an upright board.

♟ Recall, Game of Observation $18.00
Milton Bradley, 1967
Designer: Marvin Glass

Remember $15.00
Ideal, 1960s
Designer: Reuben Klamer

Robot Sam the Answer Man $30.00
Jacmar, 1950

♟ Scrabble $5.00
Selchow & Righter, 1953
Designer: Alfred Butts
All the tiles for this game have been made out of maple
from Vermont where S&R owns a wood mill.

(Pictured on next page.)

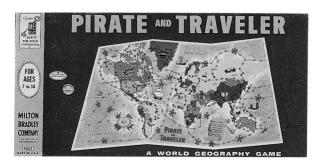

SCRABBLE FOR JUNIORS $5.00
Selchow & Righter, 1959

SCRIBBAGE $4.00
Lowe, 1967
This was similar to Scrabble, but with lettered dice.

SKIP-A-CROSS $15.00
Cadaco, 1954
And this was Cadaco's word game that played like Scrabble.

SONNY FOX FACT FINDER $25.00
Milton Bradley, 1962

SPELL IT $10.00
Cadaco, 1951
This was a game that helped kids learn to spell, multiply, add, and subtract.

SPILL & SPELL $6.00
Phillips, 1959

♟ SPOTS $23.00
Milton Bradley, 1959

STATES AND CITIES $13.00
Parker Brothers, 1955
How much did you know about the states and cities of your country? The answers were all worked into this card game.

SUSPENSE $15.00
Northwestern, 1950s
The classic game of Hangman was the basis of this game by Northwestern, a company more famous for their "Poosh-M-Up" bagatelles.

♟ SWAYZE $25.00
Milton Bradley, 1954
Hop-scotch the world for headlines in sports, politics, and diplomacy in this news game.

♟ TEN COMMANDMENTS BIBLE GAME $12.00
Cadaco, 1964
Journey through the Holy Land to be the best samaritan you can be.

♟ THINGS AND PLACES $23.00
Pressman, 1960
Designer: Bruno Furst

☗ THINK-A-TRON $75.00
Hasbro, 1961
Artwork: George Eisenberg
Wheels turned and lights flashed after you put a computer punchcard into this "Machine That Thinks Like A Man." In 1968, Hasbro re-released this as the "Mark 106 Computer."

TIC-TAC-TOE Q & A GAME $18.00
Lowell, 1957
Designer: Julie Cooper

☗ TOP SCHOLAR $22.00
Cadaco, 1957

TOP-OGRAPHY $15.00
Cadaco, 1958

☗ TREASURE HUNT $8.00
Cadaco, 1940s
Cadaco's word game was a big seller for them for many years.

UNITED STATES MAP GAME $6.00
Selchow & Righter, 1962

WHAT'S UP? $5.00
Selchow & Righter, 1970
This word game was similar to today's Wheel of Fortune.

WHAT'S WHAT $15.00
Sears, 1964
Quiz game came with a Dial-A-Matic panel and questions on history, geography, etc.

WISE OLD OWL $28.00
Novel Toy, 1950s

☗ WORD FUN $6.00
Transogram, 1955

YAHTZEE $5.00
Lowe, 1956

YOUR AMERICA $10.00
Cadaco, 1974
Answer questions about famous Americans and U.S. history to move across the scorecard.

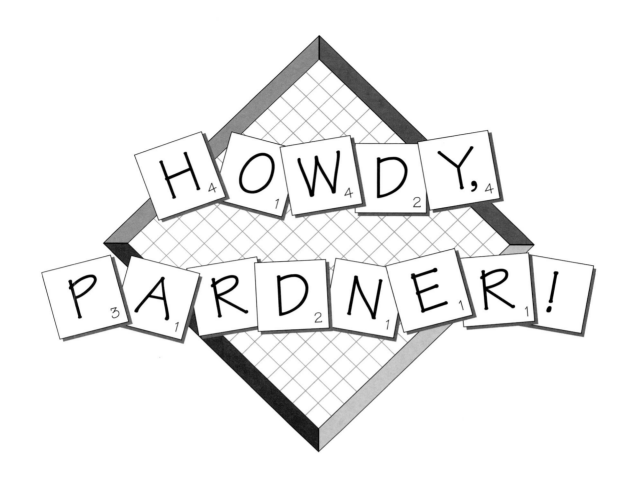

HOWDY, PARDNER!

In the mid 1950s, when Davy Crockett enthralled TV viewers on the "Disneyland" program, he started a trend that would last years and years. Believe it or not, in 1959 there were over 25 westerns on prime-time television. Western characters were basically superheroes with a horse, and their daring and heroic escapades sparked the imaginations of kids, adults, and toy manufacturers alike.

⚔"49'ERS," THE $38.00
National Games, 1950
There were two versions of this game released.
The other cover pictures a crusty, old prospec-
tor. That version is valued at $30.00.

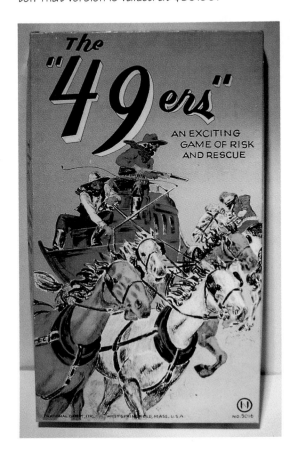

⚔ANNIE OAKLEY $35.00
Milton Bradley, 1955
Designer: Jim O'Connor
Bradley modified the artwork on its 1950 Hopa-
long Cassidy game and re-released it under the
famous cowgirl's name.

⚔ANNIE OAKLEY $40.00
Game Gems/T. Cohn, 1965
Although the TV show originally aired in the 1950s, reruns prompted
the release of this game.

⚔BANDIT TRAIL GAME FEATURING GENE AUTRY $65.00
Kenton Hardware, 1950s

BANG! A GAME OF THE OLD WILD WEST $45.00
Selchow & Righter, 1956
Designer: Julie Cooper
This was based on the story of the Dalton Gang and the Sheriffs who
shot it out with the bandits.

⚔BAT MASTERSON $50.00
Lowell, 1958
Designer: Julie Cooper

BIG CHIEF $38.00
All-Fair, 1950s

BONANZA MICHIGAN RUMMY $30.00
Parker Brothers, 1964
Artwork: Jack McMann
When Parker got the license for the Bonanza show, they photographed the cast playing the game. A week after the game was released, actor Pernell Roberts (who was pictured on the cover) left the show.

BOOTS & SADDLES $45.00
Gardner, 1958

♟ BRANDED $38.00
Milton Bradley, 1966
Designer: Jim O'Connor

BUCKAROO $27.00
Milton Bradley, 1957

BUFFALO BILL JR.'S CATTLE ROUNDUP $38.00
Built-Rite, 1956
This game, based on the 1950s TV show had a generic horse race game on the other side of the board.

CATTLE ROUND-UP $45.00
Built-Rite, 1956

CHEYENNE $20.00
Milton Bradley, 1957
This was one of Bradley's "Rainy Day Fun" games that played like Tiddley Winks.

♟♟ CHEYENNE $47.00
Milton Bradley, 1958
Designer: Jim O'Connor
A second version of this game featuring new star, Ty Hardin, standing on the cover is valued at $42.00.

CHEYENNE TARGET GAME $225.00
Mettoy, 1962
Tin litho target shows a picture of Clint Walker and comes with a dart-shooting rifle

CIMARRON STRIP $60.00
Ideal, 1967
Artwork: Ralph Pereida

♟ COWBOY ROUNDUP $25.00
Parker Brothers, 1952

COWBOYS AND INDIANS $15.00
Ed-U-Cards, 1949

COWBOYS AND INDIANS $12.00
Hasbro, 1966

DANIEL BOONE CARD GAME $20.00
Ed-U-Cards, 1965

DANIEL BOONE CARD GAME $30.00
Transogram, 1964

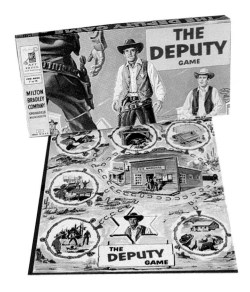

♟ GIANT WHEEL COWBOYS 'N INDIANS
    GAME $45.00
Remco, 1958

♟ DEPUTY, THE $60.00
Milton Bradley, 1960
Based on the show about a crackshot deputy who was opposed to vio-
lence. One lucky player wore a shiny silver badge until someone else
brought in a more valuable "most wanted."

♟ DOC HOLIDAY $50.00
Transogram, 1960

FASTEST GUN $27.00
Milton Bradley, 1974

FESS PARKER TARGET GAME $50.00
Transogram, 1965
Target was a large face of an Indian.

♟ FESS PARKER TRAIL BLAZERS GAME $38.00
Milton Bradley, 1964
Designer: Jim Houlihan
Game also came with a Trail Blazers Club membership application.

FESS PARKER WILDERNESS TRAIL CARD GAME $30.00
Transogram, 1964

FRONTIER FORT RESCUE GAME $25.00
Gabriel, 1955

FRONTIER MARSHALL $30.00
Saalfield, 1959

GABBY HAYES CHAMPION SHOOTING TARGET GAME $125.00
Haecker Industries, 1950
Basic target set pictured the wiry cowpoke and came with a
plastic dart gun.

♟ GENE AUTRY'S DUDE RANCH $50.00
Built-Rite, 1956

GUNFIGHT AT O.K. CORRAL $42.00
Ideal, 1973
Designer: Julie Cooper

GUNSMOKE $60.00
Lowell, 1958
Designer: Julie Cooper

GUNSMOKE TARGET GAME $95.00
Park Plastic Co., 1958

⚐ HANDS UP HARRY $45.00
Transogram, 1964
This was a 28" tall cut-out target of a Western cowpoke. When you shot his hat off, his arms came up, and when you shot his belt buckle, his pants would fall down.

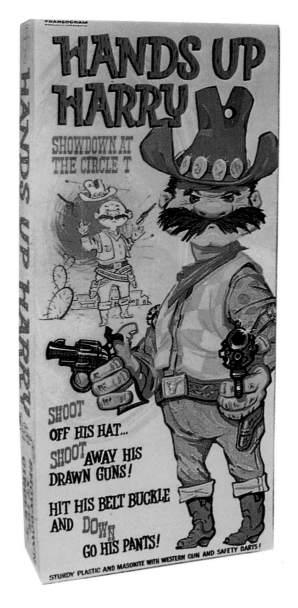

HAVE GUN WILL TRAVEL $50.00
Parker Brothers, 1959
Artwork: Lou Green

⚐ HOPALONG CASSIDY $80.00
Milton Bradley, 1950
Designer: Jim O'Connor
Milton Bradley started the lucrative TV tie-in trend with William Boyd's western hero.

HOPALONG CASSIDY CANASTA $75.00
Pacific Playing Cards, 1950

HOPALONG CASSIDY CHINESE CHECKERS $45.00
Milton Bradley, 1951
The familiar Chinese Checkers board was turned into a sheriff's badge for Hoppy's version of the classic game.

HOPALONG CASSIDY DOMINOES $75.00
Milton Bradley, 1950

HOPALONG CASSIDY LASSO GAME $75.00
Transogram, 1950

HOPALONG CASSIDY PONY EXPRESS TOSS $95.00
Transogram, 1950
This was Transogram's entry into the television market. The target, which featured Hoppy riding a jumping horse, had three large holes to toss beanbags through.

HOPALONG CASSIDY TARGET PRACTICE &
 HOLD-UP GAME $85.00
Enterprises of America, 1950

189

☕ JOHNNY RINGO $65.00
Transogram, 1960
This game was re-released a year later as Stagecoach West.

☕ LANCER $50.00
Remco, 1968

LARAMIE $58.00
Lowell, 1960
Designer: Julie Cooper

☕ LEGEND OF JESSE JAMES $52.00
Milton Bradley, 1966
A cutthroat game where kids were members of the James Gang and tried to steal saddlebags full of loot from each other.

☕ LITTLE BEAVER'S 3 GAME SET $50.00
Built-Rite, 1956
Artwork: Fred Harmon

LONE RANGER $27.00
Milton Bradley, 1966

LONE RANGER $40.00
Parker Brothers, 1956

LONE RANGER & TONTO SPIN TO WIN GAME $24.00
Pressman, 1967

LONE RANGER & THE SILVER BULLETS GAME $100.00
Gaffney, 1959

LONE RANGER SILVER BULLETS GAME $85.00
Whiting, 1956

LONE RANGER TARGET GAME $50.00
Transogram, 1967
The Lone Ranger and Tonto stop a stagecoach robbery by three magnetized bandits.

MAGNETIC COWBOY ROUNDUP $35.00
Simsco, 1950

⚘ MAIL RUN $43.00
Quality Games, 1960
Based on the TV show "Pony Express."

⚘ NOTCH $35.00
Remco, 1960

⚘ OUTLAWS, THE $60.00
Transogram, 1961

OVERLAND TRAIL $65.00
Transogram, 1960
Special standup figures in the game had a hole in which wooden bullets were placed when a player got "shot" by a bandit. This same game was also re-released for the television shows "The Virginian" and "The Outlaws."

PONY EXPRESS $35.00
Polygon, 1947

POW FRONTIER GAME $10.00
Selchow & Righter, 1955

PROSPECTOR PETE'S GAME OF GOLD RUSH $22.00
Westland Physics, 1973

RAWHIDE $80.00
Lowell, 1960
Designer: Julie Cooper

REBEL, THE $48.00
Ideal, 1961

RED RYDER'S 3 GAME SET $75.00
Built-Rite, 1956
Artwork: Fred Harmon

⚘ RESTLESS GUN $40.00
Milton Bradley, 1959
Designer: Jim O'Connor
This game was re-released a year later as Shotgun Slade.

RIFLEMAN $45.00
Milton Bradley, 1959

⚉ Rin Tin Tin $40.00
Transogram, 1955

Rodeo Wild West Game $40.00
Whitman, 1957

Round Up $45.00
All-Fair, 1946

Roy Rogers Horseshoe Set $100.00
Ohio Art, 1951

Roy Rogers Magic Play-Around Game $120.00
Amsco, 1955
This magnetic game had Roy, Dale, Pat Brady, and Bullet
chasing a bad dude around a three-dimensional cardboard town.

Roy Rogers Rodeo Game $100.00
Rogde Co., 1949
The first person to get his four men into the "Winners
Corral" won the game and got to be Roy in the next
game.

⚉ Sergeant Preston $24.00
Milton Bradley, 1956
Designer: Jim O'Connor

Sheriff of Dodge City $17.00
Parker Brothers, 1966

⚉ Shotgun Slade $40.00
Milton Bradley, 1960
Designer: Jim O'Connor
This game came out a year earlier as The Restless Gun.

STAGECOACH $40.00
Milton Bradley, 1958

STAGECOACH $30.00
Schaper, 1958

꙳ STAGECOACH WEST $50.00
Transogram, 1961
This came out a year earlier as Johnny Ringo.

STAMPEDE $25.00
Gabriel, 1956

꙳ STONEY BURKE $50.00
Transogram, 1963

꙳ STRAIGHT ARROW $44.00
Selchow & Righter, 1950
Rope steers and capture rustlers on the adventure trail
with Straight Arrow.

TEXAS RANGERS, JACE PEARSON'S
  TALES OF THE $60.00
All-Fair, 1956

TRAVELS OF JAMIE MCPHEETERS $55.00
Ideal, 1963
Follow the wagon train route from Kentucky to California.
This game was based on the 1963 TV series starring Kurt
Russell.

♟ Virginian $80.00
Transogram, 1962

♟ Wagon Train $45.00
Milton Bradley, 1960
Designer: Jim O'Connor

Wanted Dead or Alive $95.00
Lowell, 1959
Designer: Julie Cooper

Wanted Dead or Alive Target Game $250.00
Marx, 1959

♟ Wells Fargo, Tales of $62.00
Milton Bradley, 1959
Dale Robertson starred as Jim Hardie, the Wells Fargo bank agent who tracked down outlaws.

Western Roundup $25.00
Ewing, 1955

Wild Bill Hickok & Jingles
   Pony Express Game $40.00
Built-Rite, 1956
Thrifty Built-Rite usually printed another game on the back of their boards. This one had a checkerboard on the other side.

♟ Wild Bill Hickok, Calvary & Indians $50.00
Built-Rite, 1950s
Board was backed with the Game of India.

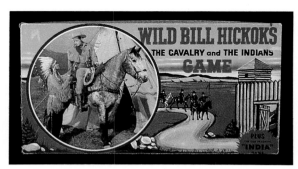

Wild Wild West $150.00
Transogram, 1966

Wyatt Earp $45.00
Transogram, 1958
Capture those filthy, stinkin' bandits and collect the rewards.

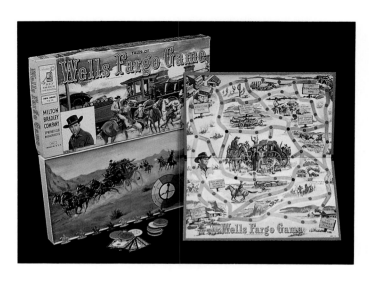

Here are the games that made you jump, flap, aim, twist, and contort all in the name of fun. Action and skill games were, and still are, a huge niche in the toy industry. These are the games that sometimes turned into fads, and every company wanted to lay claim to the newest one. They took games off the board and onto another level.

♟ AIR TRIX $22.00
Milton Bradley, 1976
Designer: Eddy Goldfarb

ANTS IN THE PANTS $8.00
Schaper, 1968
Designer: Marvin Glass & Assoc.
Tiddley Winks without the tiddley. You flipped plastic ants into the air, aiming for a large set of open trousers.

♟ BANG BOX $17.00
Ideal, 1969
Designer: Julie Cooper

BANGO! BANGO! $13.00
Schaper, 1960s
This game looked like a hollow, three-dimensional "H" with twelve marbles in it. You tried to tap the end of it with your Bango stick to get your six marbles into your channel before your opponent could.

BARNSTORMER $35.00
Marx, 1970

BARREL OF MONKEYS $4.00
Lakeside, 1969

BARREL OF MONKEYS, GIANT $12.00
Lakeside, 1969

♟ BASH $20.00
Milton Bradley, 1965
Designer: Reuben Klamer
Bash the dude with the hammer to add up points as you took out sections. If he fell over though, you were out.

BATTLE BALL $18.00
1971
In this large game, kids fired a spring-action gun at a ball to try to knock it into their opponent's goal.

BATTLING TOPS $10.00
Ideal, 1968
Designers: Eddy Goldfarb, Rene Soriano
Pull the ring and send your top spinning into the arena where it would collide with others. This classic was re-released many times under different names.

BEANBAG BUCKANEERS $28.00
Lakeside, 1960s

♟ BEE BOPPER $18.00
Ideal, 1968

♟ BIG BLAST $35.00
Transogram, 1967
You had to disarm the maze of gears, dials, and gadgets inside this big, plastic ticking bomb before time ran out.

♟ BIG SNEEZE $25.00
Ideal, 1968
Players tried to build a house of cards before a mechanical guy with allergies spun around and knocked it over with a sneeze.

BIG THUMB $14.00
Mattel, 1970
Designer: Eddy Goldfarb
Using a plastic mallet, players tried to whack their opponents who were wearing oversized foam hands.

BLOCKHEAD $8.00
Saalfield, 1954

♟ BLOP $22.00
Milton Bradley, 1966
Designer: Reuben Klamer

♟ BOBBIN NOGGIN $15.00
Milton Bradley, 1964
Game was a stunt used on the Shenanigans TV show.

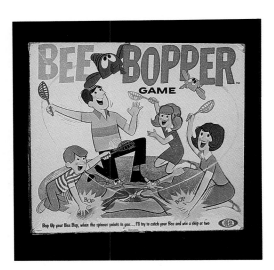

197

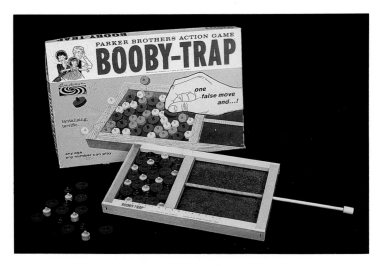

BOOB TUBE $10.00
Milton Bradley, 1962

♟ BOOBY TRAP $15.00
Parker Brothers, 1965
Designer: Sam Spahn
Artwork: Jack McMann
The skill was in recognizing where the architectural stress arches and patterns were formed once the trap was set.

BOP THE BEETLE $60.00
Ideal, 1962

BOPS AND ROBBERS $40.00
Marx, 1972
Designer: Marvin Glass & Assoc.

BOTTLE BUSTER TARGET GAME $33.00
Transogram, 1962
Pop gun pistol shot at sectioned bottles that broke apart when hit.

BUCKAROO $18.00
Ideal, 1970
Designer: Julie Cooper
Kids piled prospecting gear onto a spring-loaded mule. If it was too heavy though, he kicked it off and you were out.

BUCKET BALL $15.00
Marx, 1972

♟ BUCKET OF FUN $24.00
Milton Bradley, 1968
Designer: Marvin Glass & Assoc.
This big game shot out balls everywhere, then players raced to get as many of their color as they could.

BUCKSHOT $10.00
Parker Brothers, 1970
Designer: Marvin Glass & Assoc.

BUG OUT $8.00
Parker Brothers, 1971
You had to get the plastic bug out of a cage before another player stole it away from you.

BODY ENGLISH $15.00   ♟ BUMP BALL $20.00
Milton Bradley, 1967   *Milton Bradley, 1968*

BODY LANGUAGE $15.00   BUST 'EM TARGET GAME $60.00
Milton Bradley, 1975   *Marx, 1950s*
Cover showed Lucille Ball.

CAN-DOO $16.00
Aurora, 1971
Designer: Eddy Goldfarb
Kids tried to remove certain cans from a stack of small, plastic Campbell's soup cans without any of them falling.

CAP THE HAT $10.00
Whitman, 1965

CAREFUL $15.00
Ideal, 1967
Players tried to remove large plastic pillars from a tower without the whole thing tumbling down.

CARROM $20.00
Merdell, 1960s
This was one board that you could play many different games on from Carrom to Checkers to Crokinole and more.

♟ CASCADE $20.00
Matchbox, 1972
Artwork: Alan Rich
The cascade in the case of this game was steel balls which would drop from a tower and bounce off of a series of drums toward the scoring area.

♟ CASINO ELECTRIC PINBALL $40.00
Marx, 1971

CHARADES $7.00
Selchow & Righter, 1968

CHARADES FOR JUNIORS $5.00
Selchow & Righter, 1968

CHIPS ARE DOWN, THE $15.00
Ideal, 1970

CHOP SUEY $17.00
Ideal, 1967
As a spring-operated bowl turned, you had to pick plastic pieces from it with chopsticks.

CHUTES AWAY $20.00
Gabriel, 1977
Designer: Eddy Goldfarb

♟ CLEAN SWEEP $20.00
Schaper, 1967
Designer: Marvin Glass & Assoc.
A pop-up garbage can in the middle of this board sent a million pieces of trash everywhere which you had to sweep to your corner of the board with a plastic broom. Watch out, only "good litter" won points.

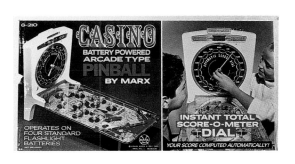

☖ COLD FEET $35.00
Ideal, 1967
Ideal's research found Mom's weren't buying this game because the last thing they wanted was their kids squirting water all over the house.

☖ CRAZY CAR RACE $18.00
Steven Mfg., 1972

☖ CRAZY CLOCK $50.00
Ideal, 1964
Artwork: Ralph Pereida
This follow-up to Mouse Trap was much more kooky and imaginative, but for some reason, the board-less game didn't prove to be as popular.

CRISS CROSS $14.00
Ideal, 1971
Designer: Eddy Goldfarb

CROSS UP, LUCILLE BALL'S $15.00
Milton Bradley, 1974

CROW HUNT $45.00
Parker Brothers, 1950s
This three-dimensional target game came with a small rifle that shot rubber bands.

DODGE BALL $15.00
Hasbro, 1973
Designers: Eddy Goldfarb, Rene Soriano

DON'T BREAK THE ICE $8.00
Schaper, 1967
Kiddies took turns knocking out "ice blocks" on a raised grid without losing the plastic man that was standing on it.

☖ DON'T BUG ME $10.00
Hasbro, 1967

DON'T COOK YOUR GOOSE $5.00
Schaper, 1971
Designer: Marvin Glass & Assoc.
Players put small plastic geese on the balanced lid of a
pot. If they tipped over, you kept 'em.

DON'T SPILL THE BEANS $8.00
Schaper, 1967

DOWN THE DRAIN $6.00
Schaper, 1974
All of your money was at the bottom of a drain. You had
to lower a hook on a string through the grating to
retrieve as much as you could.

☃ DRAG STRIP $15.00
Milton Bradley, 1965

DROP IN THE BUCKET $15.00
Milton Bradley, 1960s
Designer: Reuben Klamer

☃ DYNAMITE SHACK $33.00
Milton Bradley, 1968
Designer: Marvin Glass & Assoc.
According to MB executives, no other game at the time
tested as well as Dynamite Shack. Kids were delighted with
the game where sticks of explosives were dropped into a
shack before it blew up. Unfortunately, there was a backlash
against it by parents' groups, who claimed it was too violent
and, get this, might encourage terrorism.

☃ EGG RACE $20.00
Ideal, 1968

ELECTRIC HOT POTATO $30.00
Electric Game Co., 1960
Designer: Jim Prentice

ELECTRIC JACK STRAWS $12.00
Electric Game Co., 1950s
Designer: Jim Prentice
Prentice's variation of Jack Straws or Pick-Up Sticks had
players using tweezers to try to pick up the nearly hidden
straws from a metal can with holes in the top. If you touched
the cover though, a buzzer sounded and a light flashed.

☃ FANG BANG $18.00
Milton Bradley, 1967
Designer: Marvin Glass & Assoc.

FASCINATION $20.00
Remco, 1961
Two players raced marbles through hand-held mazes to light
up a tower they were connected to.

FASCINATION POOL $20.00
Remco, 1962
Players held the 17" x 12" board in their hands and tried to
direct the balls to the corresponding colored pockets.

♟ FAST EDDIE $10.00
Mattel, 1970
Designers: Eddy Goldfarb, Rene Soriano
Players aimed a plastic kid that shot marbles in an attempt to
knock the most marbles out of the playing ring.

♟ FLAP JACK $18.00
Remco, 1958   (Pictured on next page.)

♟ FEELEY MEELEY $22.00
Milton Bradley, 1967
Designer: Marvin Glass & Assoc.
Game was a large box with a hole on each side. A card was
turned, signaling all players to simultaneously find the item
shown...by touch!

FIRE ALARM $10.00
Milton Bradley, 1970

♟ FISH BAIT $50.00
Ideal, 1965
Designer: M. Glass & Assoc.
Ideal's final entry in their Gold-
bergian trilogy had an unlucky
angler in the title role.

♟ FIVE WISE BIRDS $30.00
Parker Brothers, 1954
They don't look so smart to me.

♟ FLEA CIRCUS $35.00
Mattel, 1964
You had to make your magnetic fleas hop on a tightrope,
ride a unicycle, perform trapeze acts, and do other stunts
in Mattel's cool game.   (Pictured on next page.)

FLIP IT JACKPOT $45.00
Aurora, 1973
Designer: Marvin Glass
    & Assoc.
This was a cross between
Pachinko and a slot machine.
The box pictured Flip Wilson
on its cover.

FLIP THE FROG $20.00
Transogram, 1963
Flip the frog into the lily pad
target with the stick and win
the game.

⚱ FRANTIC FROGS $25.00

Milton Bradley, 1965

Designers: Reuben Klamer, Dick Miller

At one point, this was designed to use real frogs that you would send away for, much like an ant farm. When that proved to be too complicated, tin, wind-up ones from Japan were imported.

⚱ FREEFALL $20.00

Hasbro, 1968

Not the tallest, but as the cover states, "One of the tallest games in the world!"

FRISKY FROG $35.00

Transogram, 1962

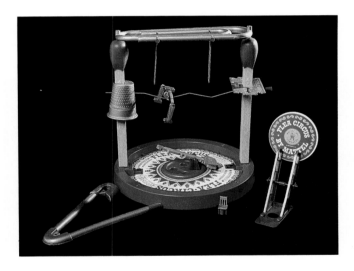

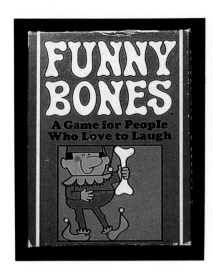

♟ FUNNY BONES $12.00
Parker Brothers, 1968
Artwork: Jack McMann

♟ FUNNY FINGER $16.00
Ideal, 1968

♟ GETAWAY CHASE GAME $60.00
DX, 1968
Your motorized 1920s gangster-style cars chased each other through the cardboard streets of Chicago.

GNIP GNOP $10.00
Parker Brothers, 1971
Designer: Marvin Glass & Assoc.
Artwork: Jack McMann
This variation of Ping Pong was one of Parker Brothers first successful action games. Gnip Gnop is Ping Pong spelled backwards.

♟ GO BACK $15.00   ♟ HATS OFF $14.00
Milton Bradley, 1967   Kohner, 1967

♟ GOLD TRAIL $15.00
Hasbro, 1966

♟ GRAB A LOOP $24.00
Milton Bradley, 1968
Designer: Chuck Foley

GRAND SLAM $15.00
Ideal, 1969
Designer: Reuben Klamer

♟ GREAT ESCAPE $22.00
Ideal, 1967
Actually, this is the antithesis of an activity game. Players were handcuffed to the game board and had to search for the key that would set them free.

♟ HANDS DOWN $20.00
Ideal, 1964
Designer: Marvin Glass & Assoc.
Artwork: Ralph Pereida
This basic card game turned into a hit thanks to Ideal's Slam-O-Matic.

HANG ON HARVEY $18.00
Ideal, 1969
Designer: Reuben Klamer
You took Harvey from top to bottom by moving pegs on a clear upright board. If he fell, it was back to the top.

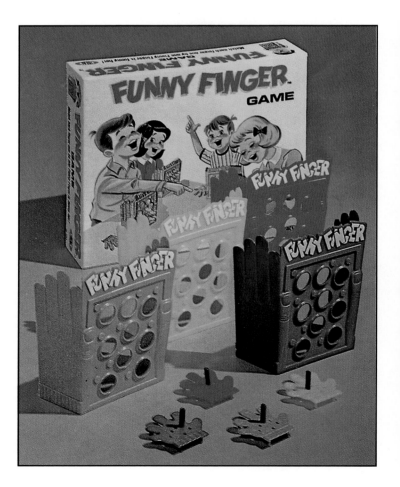

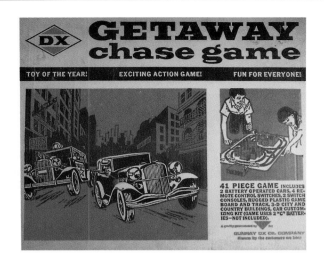

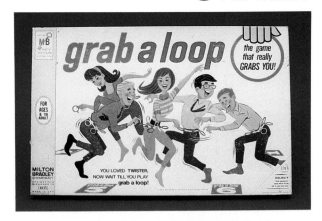

♟ HIP FLIP $23.00

Parker Brothers, 1968
Designer: Marvin Glass & Assoc.

♟ HOT POTATO $24.00

Remco, 1959

♟ HOOPLA $38.00

Ideal, 1966
The teetering unicyclist would zip around this big game to catch disks worth points.

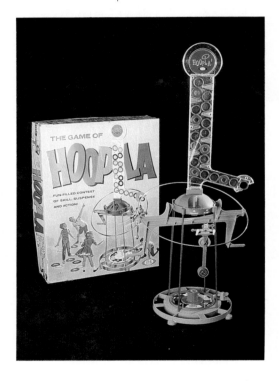

♟ HUNGRY HENRY $20.00

Ideal, 1969

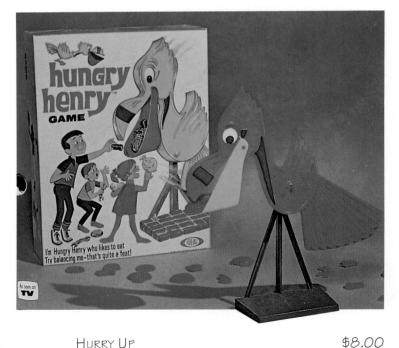

HOP AND STOMP $20.00

Kenner, 1969

HOP N' POP $18.00

Transogram, 1964
Jump the ball from hole to hole to the top of the hill to ring the bell and score.

HURRY UP $8.00

Parker Brothers, 1971
Push your marbles to the top of a plastic pyramid grid. First one up, won.

HURRY, WAITER $20.00

Ideal, 1967

JACK STRAWS $4.00
Parker Brothers, 1950s
This is what Pick-Up Sticks was called in the old days.

JUNGLE FUN $20.00
Transogram, 1968
A safari in your own living room as you catapulted magnetic pieces toward a jungle target.

JUNGLE HUNT $65.00
Hubley, 1964
Designer: Marvin Glass & Assoc.
This large plastic target game had animals popping up from behind trees and bushes.

☖ JUNGLE SKITTLES $45.00
American Toy Works, 1950s

☖ JUNK YARD, THE $18.00
Ideal, 1975
Pictures of garbage would pop up when you hit the targets in this pinball type game.

☖ KABOOM $18.00
Ideal, 1966
Artwork: Ralph Pereida
This was another game that caused concern among Ideal executives. They were worried that parents wouldn't buy it, fearing bits of exploding balloon might blind their kids. You can almost hear the designer's mother crying: "Don't invent that, you'll put someone's eye out!"

KARATE TOPS $12.00
Ideal, 1971
Designers: Eddy Goldfarb, Rene Soriano
New spring-loaded tops fought in this updated version of Ideal's Battling Tops.

☖ KERPLUNK $20.00
Ideal, 1967
Designer: Eddy Goldfarb
Artwork: Ralph Pereida
Players removed sticks from a tower filled with marbles while trying not to let them fall.

KICKBACK $10.00
Schaper, 1965

KIKIT SKITTLES $25.00
Carrom, 1966

KING OF THE MOUNTAIN $17.00
Saalfield, 1957

KNOCK OFF $30.00
Kenner, 1969

KNOCK THE CLOCK $15.00
Ideal, 1971
Designer: Eddy Goldfarb

KNOCK YOUR BLOCK OFF $30.00
Hasbro, 1964

♟ KOOKY CARNIVAL $15.00
Milton Bradley, 1969
Designer: Marvin Glass & Assoc.

LA RIGA $8.00
Selchow & Righter, 1957
Magnetic game where you tried to pull pins into a fenced in area of the board.

♟ LAST STRAW, THE $15.00
Schaper, 1966

LEAPIN' LIZARD $15.00
Ideal, 1971
Designer: Eddy Goldfarb

♟ LIMBO LEGS $30.00
Milton Bradley, 1969
Designers: Larry Reiner, Marvin Glass & Assoc.

♟ LOLLI PLOP $10.00
Milton Bradley, 1962
Designer: Skip Hoyland

♟ LOOK OUT BELOW $20.00
Ideal, 1968

♟ LOVE $20.00
Hasbro, 1968
Twister for flower children. The first one to spell out
"love" on all fours was the winner.

LUCKY LOUIE $25.00
Transogram, 1968
This roaring 20s gangster target dared you to shoot
the silver dollars and ace of spades out of his hands.

LUCKY STAR GUMBALL GAME $40.00
Ideal, 1961
Put a penny in and try to maneuver the gumball out of
the ramps. The commercial for this sang "You pay... you
play... you chew away... you save more pennies everyday!"

MAGIC SHOT SHOOTING GALLERY $28.00
Marx, 1974
Enclosed shooting gallery contained a magnetic pistol
that grabbed pellets through the clear front cover and
shot them at a variety of targets.

MAGNATEL $18.00
Mattel, 1961
A number of games could be played on this board resembling a pool table that used magnetic and non-magnetic
disks.

♟ MARBLE MAZE $15.00
Hasbro, 1966

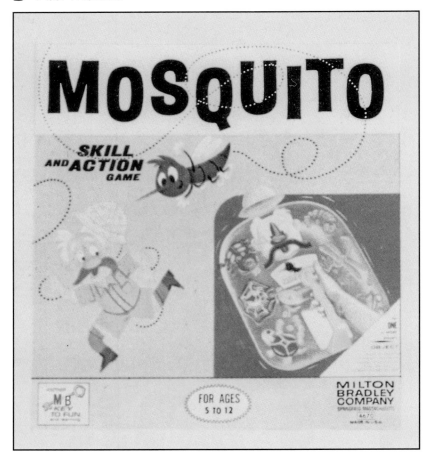

MARBLEHEAD $20.00

Ideal, 1969

This was the opposite of Ideal's earlier successful marble game, KerPlunk, in that you tried to get the most marbles to fall out of a clear plastic head.

MASTER SPY TARGET GAME $33.00

Transogram, 1965

Shoot out the headlights on the criminal's car and your score would automatically appear.

MEATBALL THE HUNGRY LION BALL TOSS GAME $26.00

Transogram, 1964

MONKEY'S UNCLE $18.00

Transogram, 1967

The player who completed all of the activities pictured on the "Monkey Mats" around the room first was the winner in this stunt game.

♟ MOSQUITO $20.00

Milton Bradley, 1966

Designer: Marvin Glass & Assoc.

♟ MOTHER HEN TARGET GAME $25.00

STS, 1970

♟ MOUSE TRAP $50.00

Ideal, 1963

Designers: Marvin Glass & Assoc.,
  Sid Sackson

Artwork: Ralph Pereida

Glass originally brought this to Ideal as a toy. However, Ideal president Lionel Weintraub thought he could build a better Mouse Trap by turning it into a game and brought Sackson on to add the game play to Glass' original contraption.

MOUSIE MOUSIE $10.00

Spears, 1963

ODYSSEY $45.00

Magnavox, 1972

Designer: Ralph Baer

This first home video game came with foil cards to play over a dozen basic games. Since there were no graphics, plastic overlays were included to place on your TV screen.

OH NO! $17.00
Milton Bradley, 1966

♟ OH, NUTS! $22.00
Ideal, 1969
Designer: Marvin Glass & Assoc.
Bluff your way to collect three marbles of the same color hidden under plastic nutshells.

♟ ON GUARD $13.00
Parker Brothers, 1967
This game tilted up and down and right and left as you tried to maneuver a ball into your opponents goal.

♟ ON THE BALL $15.00
Milton Bradley, 1964

OOP STIX $10.00
Transogram, 1966

♟ OPERATION $18.00
Milton Bradley, 1965
Suggested by Harvey-Carlson
Designer: Marvin Glass & Assoc.
This was originally a stunt on the TV show "Shenanigans."

PADDLE POOL $12.00
Milton Bradley, 1974

PAR-A-SHOOT $30.00
Baldwin, 1940s

♟ PARTY STUNTS $12.00
Milton Bradley, 1953

PENDULUM BOWL $25.00
Aurora, 1974

PENDULUM POOL $20.00
Aurora, 1974
A pendulum was placed behind the cue ball and swung to sink the ten numbered balls.

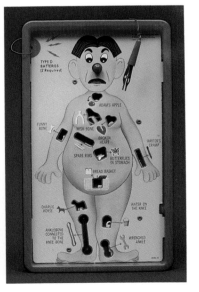

PENGUIN POLO $25.00
Hasbro, 1968

PERFECTION $8.00
Lakeside, 1973
You had 60 seconds to fit 26 plastic pieces into the correct slots before the timer ran out and popped everything into the air.

♟ PIE FACE $30.00
Ideal, 1966
The prototype pictured here shows that Hasbro couldn't decide on a name for their new action game. Here, players stuck their faces in a target and spun to see how many times they had to turn a crank which activated a spring-loaded arm holding a pie.

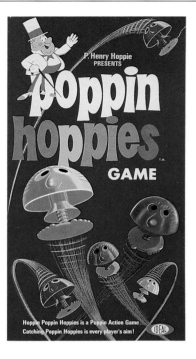

PING BALL $15.00
Parker Brothers, 1964
This game was a combination of Ping Pong and Tetherball.

PITCHIN' PAL $15.00
Cadaco, 1953

PLINKETY PLUNK $25.00
Electric Game Co., 1957
Designer: Jim Prentice

POM POM GAME $15.00
Epoch, 1968

POP-ZA-BALL TARGET GAME $38.00
Mattel, 1961

POPCORN $25.00
Marx, 1976

♟ POPPIN' HOPPIES $15.00
Ideal, 1968
Designer: Eddy Goldfarb

♟ POST OFFICE $18.00
Hasbro, 1968

POT O' GOLD $45.00
Transogram, 1962

POW WOW $10.00
Parker Brothers, 1973
Designer: Marvin Glass & Assoc. This was Parker's flapping, clapping, rhythm game.

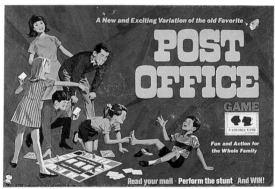

♟ PULL THE RUG OUT $15.00
Schaper, 1968
Designer: Reuben Klamer

PYRAMID $15.00
Schaper, 1959

QUICK SHOOT $15.00
Ideal, 1971
Designer: Marvin Glass & Assoc.

RACING TOPS $20.00
Ideal, 1974
Designers: Eddy Goldfarb, Rene Soriano
Here, the Battling Tops variation fought each other as they went along a plastic race course.

☖ REBOUND $20.00
Ideal, 1971
Designer: Julie Cooper

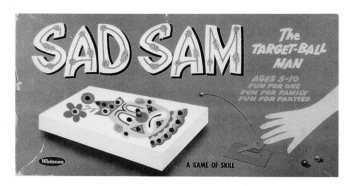

ROLLARINO $22.00
Transogram, 1962
This game was retitled a year later as "Big Payoff."

ROLLER COASTER $18.00
Milton Bradley, 1973

☖ SAD SAM THE TARGET BALL MAN $10.00
Whitman, 1966

SCAT TARGET GAME $45.00
1950
When you hit the bullseye on the tin litho fence, a cat would spring into the air.

☖ SCR-UNCH $45.00
Mattel, 1967   (Pictured on next page.)

SHARPSHOOTER $37.00
Cadaco, 1951
Hit the big game animals on the target and watch them reverse into mounted trophies showing your score.

RIDE THE RODS $10.00
1971
A challenge of coordination and dexterity as two rods were pulled apart and a large steel ball rolled uphill.

ROAD RACE SKILL DRIVE GAME $30.00
Tarco, 1963
Cardboard track had a magnet underneath that let you drive you car through obstacles by magnetic remote control.

☖ ROCK'EM SOCK'EM ROBOTS $125.00
Marx, 1966
Designer: Marvin Glass & Assoc.
One of the coolest! What else can you say? Versions after 1971 came unassembled in a smaller box and are valued at $70.00.

SHUFFLE KING　　　　$30.00
Marx, 1960s

SHUFFLE WINKS　　　$7.00
Selchow & Righter, 1959
Game board combined Tiddley Winks
and Shuffleboard on one side and a
Bagatelle type game using Tiddley
Winks on the other.

☙ SILLY SAFARI　　　$48.00
Topper, 1966
Mouse Trap with a wacky jungle
theme. Topper's entry into the 3-D
game craze had kids using bare-foot-
ed playing pieces to stalk wild animals. This was one of the few games
manufactured by the New Jersey-
based toy company.

☙ SKEE BALL　　　$30.00
Eldon, 1963
Pull the plunger and the ball whizzed
up the ramp toward the target
rings. Game had automatic scoring
and ball return.

SKILL BALL　　　$25.00
Pressman, 1950

SKILL-IT　　　$15.00
Milton Bradley, 1966
Designer: Skip Hoyland

SKITTLE BINGO　　　$25.00
Aurora, 1973

☙ SKITTLE BOWL　　　$20.00
Aurora, 1969

SKITTLE BOWL,
　OLYMPIC SIZE　　　$30.00
Aurora, 1971

SKITTLE HORSESHOES　$30.00
Aurora, 1973
Designer: Marvin Glass & Assoc.

SKITTLE POKER　　　$25.00
Aurora, 1974

☖ SKITTLE POOL $28.00
Aurora, 1972
Here, a cue ball was positioned next to a "magic cue" under a skittle stand. When the skittle was pulled back and released it hit the "magic cue" which hit the cue ball which... well you can figure it out from there.

☖ SKITTLE SCORE-BALL, ALL AMERICAN $13.00
Aurora, 1972

SKITTLE SHOOT-OUT $30.00
Aurora, 1974

SKITTLE TIC-TAC-TOE $20.00
Aurora, 1973

SKITTLES $20.00
Merdel, 1962

SKULLY $15.00
Ideal, 1961
Thump your discs through twelve squares on a large plastic mat to win.

SLAM BACK $10.00
Milton Bradley, 1974
A table-top cousin of handball, players gripped blocks and used them to slam a ball into a rubber cushion and back to the other guy's side.

SLAP HAPPY $15.00
Ideal, 1971
Designers: Eddy Goldfarb, Rene Soriano

☖ SLAP STICK $20.00
Milton Bradley, 1967
Designer: Reuben Klamer

☖ SLAP TRAP $25.00
Ideal, 1967
Designer: Marvin Glass & Assoc.
Slow moving players whose beetles got caught in the trap had to pay the Trapper to get their beetle back.

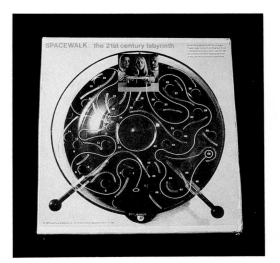

♟ SPACEWALK $13.00
Selchow & Righter, 1970
Adjustable knobs controlled the ball as it was manipulated through a maze. Watch out for the holes that would make you lose the ball.

SPIDER'S MAZE $14.00
Transogram, 1966
A spring-loaded spider flew into the air when you maneuvered a steel ball through his maze to the hole he was guarding.

SPIN THE BOTTLE $18.00
Hasbro, 1968

SLICK SHOOTER PENNY ARCADE GAME $35.00
Mattel, 1974

♟ SMACK-A-ROO $35.00
Mattel, 1964
Mattel's large set boasted "a new game for each day in the week... plus 4 for Sunday!"

♟ SNAKE'S ALIVE $23.00
Ideal, 1966
Designers: Eddy Goldfarb, Rene Soriano
You want those oriental rubies. But you must poke your finger in the snake basket. Will the spring-loaded snake jump out at you? Must you take all those baby snakes instead of the rubies you're seeking? This game asks more questions than an annoying kid.

SNAKES IN THE GRASS $15.00
Kohner, 1960

♟ SPACE ELECTRIC PINBALL $50.00
Marx, 1971

SPUDSIE $25.00
1960s
This plastic wind-up potato with the happy face would get batted and thrown around until his timer went off.

SPY'S-A-POPPIN $60.00
Transogram, 1965
The object of this large, super cool target game was to knock out a spy descending a staircase before he reached the bottom and detonated a bomb that sent a captive girl flying through the air.

STEADY EDDIE $22.00
Milton Bradley, 1962

STEP LIVELY SHUFFLEBOARD $15.00
Marx, 1972

SUPER CROW SHOOT $35.00
Jaymar, 1958

SUPER MAGNATEL $22.00
Mattel, 1966

SWACK $30.00
Ideal, 1968

SWIVEL $23.00
Milton Bradley, 1972
Designer: Ted Starcewski

SYNCRON-8 $25.00
Transogram, 1963
A control button on this large game started a center disc spinning, and by synchronizing the speed, marbles were thrown into target areas.

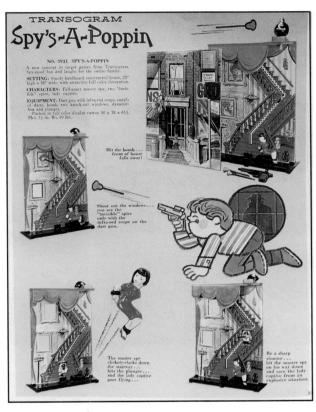

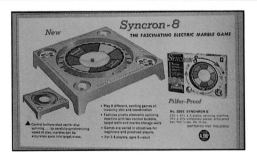

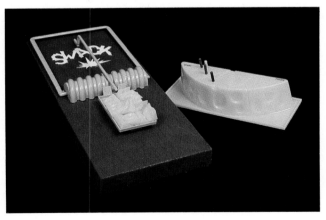

217

♟ Tantalizer $30.00

Northern Signal, 1960s

This optical puzzle game had you try to do stunts of dexterity while looking into a mirror. The instructions advised you to have plenty of tranquilizers on hand and asked throughout the rules, "How are your pills holding out?"

Temple of Fu Manchu $25.00

Pressman, 1967

Think Thunk $12.00

Milton Bradley, 1973

♟ Three Keys to Treasure Bagatelle $60.00

Marx, 1960

Tie & Tangle $20.00

Hasbro, 1967

♟ Tiger Island $50.00

Ideal, 1966

Designer: Marvin Glass & Assoc.

Castaways flung marbles into the spinning tiger's mouth to stop him from clobbering them.

♟ Tight Squeeze $26.00

Mattel, 1967

Designer: Marvin Glass & Assoc.

Two couples, hitched together in giant connecting belts had to try to take the belt off in different variations. The first couple to complete it, had to cinch the belt one notch tighter. Winner was couple who got five points... or passed out last!

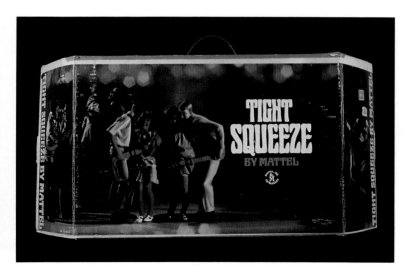

TIGRRRR SCORE-A-MATIC BALL TOSS $28.00
Transogram, 1966
When you tossed a ball into the plastic tigers mouth on this 20" target, the score-a-matic would register and the ball would be returned to you through a chute in the front.

♟ TILT SCORE $15.00
Schaper, 1964

♟ TILTIN' MILTON $28.00
Ideal, 1968
Designer: Julie Cooper

TILTY $15.00
Whitman, 1967
Designer: Reuben Klamer

♟ TIME BOMB $40.00
Milton Bradley, 1964
Designer: Marvin Glass & Assoc.
This was Marvin Glass' first game for Milton Bradley.

♟ TIN CAN ALLEY $45.00
Ideal, 1976
The cover of this target set featured Chuck Connors.

219

⌂ TIP IT $18.00
Ideal, 1965
Designer: Marvin Glass & Assoc.
Artwork: Ralph Pereida
This popular balancing game was re-released in the
1990s and is still fun to play!

⌂ TIT TAT TOE $12.00
Parker Brothers, 1950s

TOP IT $17.00
Ideal, 1972
Designers: Eddy Goldfarb, Rene Soriano

TOP THE TOP $15.00
Ideal, 1971
Designer: Reuben Klamer
This game found out who could balance the most spin-
ning tops onto one another.

TORNADO BOWL $15.00
Ideal, 1971
This was simply a re-working of Battling Tops but this
one had obstacles in the course.

TOSS ACROSS $20.00
Ideal, 1969
Designer: Marvin Glass & Assoc.

TRIP HAMMER $12.00
Milton Bradley, 1974
Designer: Marvin Glass & Assoc.

⌂ TRIP TRAP $45.00
Remco, 1969

TUGGY $35.00
A.C. Gilbert, 1960s
In this game, a turtle with a head on either end moved
and spun between two finish lines.

TUMBLE BUMBLE $15.00
Ideal, 1970
You slid giant capsules down a ramp and into a spinning
chamber to score points.

TUSSLE $15.00
Milton Bradley, 1960s
Designer: Reuben Klamer

⌂ TWISTER $15.00
Milton Bradley, 1966
Designer: Chuck Foley
Milton Bradley's sales department thought the top
brass was absolutely nuts to even consider this game.
However, Twister turned out to be one of the company's
biggest sellers.

☖ TWIZZLE $14.00

Schaper, 1964

Aim the spiral marble-shooter and bowl marbles into the scoring gates. Don't bowl a marble in the same gate twice or you'll lose points.

UP 'N OVER $15.00

Ideal, 1971

Designer: Eddy Goldfarb

Each of the twelve segments of the round plastic board would catapult a ball on a string to the other side. Players scored when they flipped the ball through a hole in the other guy's segment.

WHIPLASH $15.00

1967

This was a 16 inch dual-action skee ball game that two players would play at once.

☖ WHIRL OUT $17.00

Milton Bradley, 1971

Designer: Reuben Klamer

Each player attempted to get all of his marbles to stay on a large upright spinning wheel to win the game.

☖ WHIZ BOWL $15.00

Zenith, 1950s

WHOOPS $20.00

Aurora, 1968

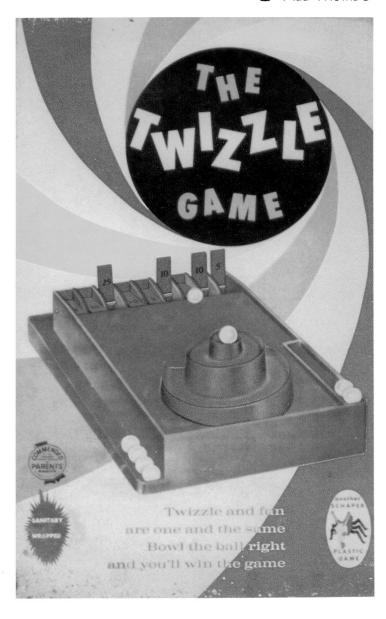

WING DING $15.00
Cadaco, 1951
Kids would catapult a weighted badminton-type shuttlecock toward a target board.

WING IT $10.00
Schaper, 1971
Target game contained two launchers that shot plastic discs.

WRESTLE AROUND $17.00
Ideal, 1969
Designers: Eddy Goldfarb, Rene Soriano
This was a large four handled plastic arena that everyone would drop a marble into then try to keep it from falling through a hole on the center.

♟ YERTLE, GAME OF $75.00
Revell, 1960
Artwork: Theodore Giesel

ZIG ZAG ZOOM $20.00
Ideal, 1970
Designers: Eddy Goldfarb, Rene Soriano

ZINGO $20.00
Empire Plastics, 1950s

♟ ZOK $25.00
Hasbro, 1967

Think back... vacation time at the old homestead. The family piles in the car and takes to the asphalt highway. After ten minutes, the trees and cows begin to drift hypnotically, slow mo, past the car window. Your eyelids are turning to lead, narcolepsy is setting in. You're even a bit nauseous, and you're wondering: are we there yet? Next time, perhaps the family should simply stay home and play one of the many travel and adventure games that have been produced over the years. As far back as 1822, toy manufacturers began providing an array of travel games for families. These games offered the allure of going "around the world," or going where no one had been before — to a remote mountain peak or an exotic desert — without leaving the living room.

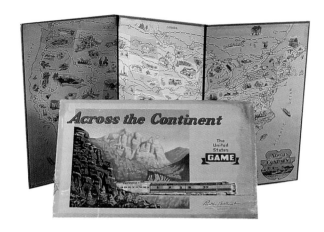

♟ ACROSS THE CONTINENT $50.00
Parker Brothers, 1952
Players toured the U.S. from coast to coast on a three-fold map that showed railroad routes, crops, and industries of various regions of the country.

♟ ACROSS THE USA $15.00
Hasbro, 1966

AIR RACE AROUND THE WORLD $30.00
Lido, 1950

ALLSTATE TRAVEL GAME $17.00
Sears, 1964
A game designed to take on long trips for the kids. One drawback was the piles of loose play money and deck of cards.

AMERICAN AIRLINES TRAVEL GAMES $38.00
Milton Bradley, 1955

♟ AMOCO MILEAGE GAME $12.00
Cadaco, 1976

AROUND THE WORLD TRAVEL GAME $10.00
Golden Rock, 1975

ASTRO WORLD GAME $20.00
American Airlines, 1971

♟ ASTRON $62.00
Parker Brothers, 1955
Parker Brothers changed the name to Skylanes in 1956 because it was more representational of the game. Astron sounded like it involved space travel.

AUTO BINGO $2.00
Regal, 1966
Regal also had a large line of variations of Auto Bingo.

AUTOFUN $35.00
Milton Bradley, 1963
This big game came with a plastic track and cardboard town that motorized cars raced around, picking up points and "voiding" other players points.

⚓ BIG TOWN $40.00
Milton Bradley, 1962
Designer: Ted Starcewski
Children traveled about town with their magnetic cars. The game included a driving test to see who could zip through town faster.

CAPITAL AIR RACE $40.00
Capital Airlines, 1955

⚓ CAR TRAVEL GAME $18.00
Milton Bradley, 1958
Designer: Jim O'Connor

CHEVYLAND SWEEPSTAKES $37.00
Milton Bradley, 1968

⚓ COAST TO COAST $18.00
Ewing, 1955

CONEY ISLAND $40.00
Selchow & Righter, 1956
Designer: Julie Cooper
With a handful of dimes, players tried to ride all of the rides and still have money left to spend on concessions.

COOK'S TOUR $14.00
Selchow & Righter, 1972
European travel game where souvenir cards were picked up for points. Bonus coins were awarded for answering questions — sometimes in a foreign language.

FIND-A-CAR BINGO $2.00
Regal, 1966

FLAGSHIP AIR FREIGHT $45.00
Milton Bradley, 1946

FLIGHT CAPTAIN $20.00
Lowe, 1972
Travel around the world on a plastic board resembling a larger version of the game, "Trouble."

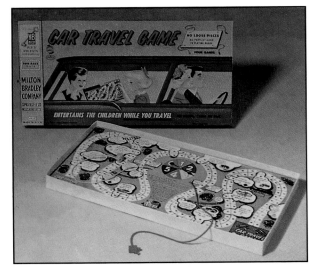

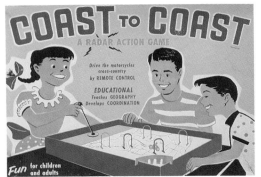

FLIP FOR FUN $5.00
Parker Brothers, 1966
This was another game designed for those fidgety kids who couldn't sit still on long trips.

FUN PLACES OF THE
   U.S.A. $5.00
Tee Pee Toys, 1978

GAME OF
   LANDMARKS $10.00
Selchow & Righter, 1962

GET THAT LICENSE $40.00
Selchow & Righter, 1955
The board was a map of the U.S. with auto routes from state to state. You learned license plates and state capitals while piling up your score.

GLOBAL AIR RACE $65.00
Replogle Globes, 1952
This around-the-world travel game came complete with a metal globe and magnetic planes.

GLOBE-TROTTERS $35.00
Selchow & Righter, 1948

HOLIDAY $45.00
Replogle Globes, 1958

INTERNATIONAL AIRPORT
   GAME $25.00
Magic Wand, 1964

⚓ INTERSTATE HIGHWAY $35.00
Selchow & Righter, 1963
Travel across the country on the "roads of to-morrow." The winner was the one who had the most money at the end of his trip. Basically, the cheap guy who wouldn't spring for hotels or food won.

(Pictured on next page.)

JET RACE	$15.00	
Built-Rite, 1960s		
JET WORLD	$13.00	
Milton Bradley, 1975		
♟ LET'S DRIVE	$15.00	
Milton Bradley, 1967		
♟ LET'S TAKE A TRIP	$18.00	
Milton Bradley, 1963		
LICENSE NUMBER BINGO	$2.00	
Regal, 1966		
MAGIC MILES	$20.00	
Hasbro, 1956		

MARINE WORLD	$20.00
Parker Brothers, 1968	
MATCHBOX TRAFFIC GAME	$45.00
Bronner, 1968	
MT. EVEREST	$32.00
Gabriel, 1955	
OFFICIAL DRIVERS ED GAME	$17.00
Cadaco, 1973	
♟ SEE NEW YORK 'ROUND THE TOWN GAME	$50.00
Transogram, 1964	

SEE THE U.S.A. GAME $17.00
Cadaco, 1968

SKY LANES $50.00
Parker Brothers, 1956
Originally released as Astron one year earlier.

⚺ SPOT A CAR BINGO $17.00
Hasbro, 1950s

SPOT-A-PLATE $30.00
Fairchild, 1953
This game contained cardboard license plates from every state.

TAXI $38.00
Selchow & Righter, 1961

TOURING $5.00
Parker Brothers, 1954

⚺ TRADE WINDS $30.00
Parker Brothers, 1960

TRAFFIC $20.00
Lowe, 1968
Lowe's game taught traffic safety and good driving habits.

⚺ TRAFFIC JAM $45.00
Harett-Gilmar, 1954

TRAFFIC SAFETY
    BINGO $2.00
Regal, 1966

⚺ TRAVEL $30.00
Gardner, 1950s

TRAVEL AMERICA $28.00
Jacmar, 1950

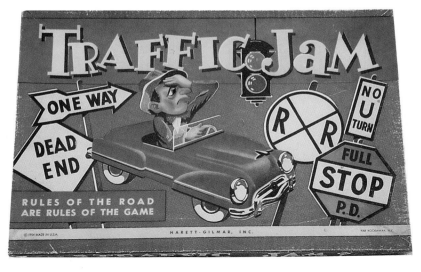

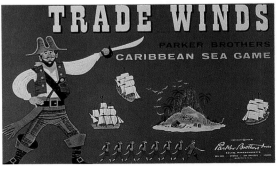

♟ UNDERSEA WORLD OF
    JACQUES COUSTEAU $22.00
Parker Brothers, 1968

♟ WIPE OFF TARGET GAME $12.00
Milton Bradley, 1959
The box claimed this game was "great for kids while you travel."

♟ WORLD'S FAIR PANORAMA GAME $45.00
Milton Bradley, 1964
Designer: Doug Beck

♟ WIDE WORLD $35.00
Parker Brothers, 1957

♟ WORLD'S FAIR GAME $38.00
Milton Bradley, 1964
Designer: Doug Beck
Game contained a 20" x 22" playing mat that featured many of the attractions at New York's big event.

   WORLD'S FAIR CHILDREN'S GAME $20.00
   Ed-U-Cards, 1964

Our final chapter encompasses games of strategy. It also includes a conglomeration of games that defy categorization.

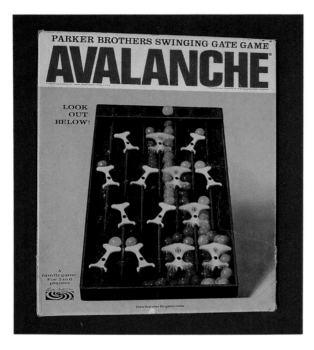

10-4 GOOD BUDDY $8.00
Parker Brothers, 1976
Ouch! A game about the nadir of American civilization — the CB Radio craze!

4-CYTE $6.00
Milton Bradley, 1967

♟ **7 CARD STUD** $15.00
Hasbro, 1973
Cover showed Jerry Lewis.

ACEY DEUCEY $10.00
Selchow & Righter, 1948
The board contained backgammon on one side and checkers on the other.

AGGRAVATION $5.00
Co-5, 1966
Parchesi type game with marbles. When two players landed in the same hole one had to go back to the start — and that was aggravatin'!

AND THEN THERE WERE NONE $50.00
Ideal, 1967

ANIMAL TRAP $30.00
Multiple Products, 1950s

ARABIAN NIGHTS $30.00
National Games, 1950

♟ **AVALANCHE** $7.00
Parker Brothers, 1966
Designer: Sam Spahn

AVANTE $7.00
Fyanes, 1967
This game combined the elements of Checkers and Gin Rummy.

♟ **BALAROO** $15.00
Milton Bradley, 1967

BANTU $17.00
Parker Brothers, 1955

♟ BEHIND THE 8 BALL $15.00
Selchow & Righter, 1969

♟ BERMUDA TRIANGLE $20.00
Milton Bradley, 1976
Designers: Jim Houlihan, Bill Burke

BIG GAME $44.00
National Games, 1950
Artwork: Gillette French

BIG GAME HUNT $30.00
Carrom, 1947

♟ BING CROSBY, CALL ME LUCKY $48.00
Parker Brothers, 1954
Players attempted to capture their opponent's number cards on a board laid out in squares. A "Lucky Seven" card added suspense to the game as well.

♟ BINGO-MATIC $8.00
Transogram, 1960
There were a million different sets of Bingo on the market. Most are valued under $10.00.

BLUFF   **$22.00**
Saalfield, 1963
Artwork: Ed Hungerford
This dice game took advantage of the headlines of the time and pictured JFK and Khrushchev on the cover trying to outwit each other.

BOUNDARY   **$10.00**
Mattel, 1970

BRAINSTORM   **$8.00**
Lowe, 1972

BREAKTHROUGH   **$10.00**
3M, 1965

BRICKO   **$17.00**
Saalfield, 1953

BRIDGE FOR JUNIORS   **$4.00**
Selchow & Righter, 1961

BRIDGE-IT   **$13.00**
Hasbro, 1960
Object was to complete a continuous path of bridges from one end of the board to the other without your opponent blocking your path. The bridges fit into slots on raised towers on the plastic board.

♟ **CALLING ALL CARS**   **$18.00**
Parker Brothers, 1959

♟ **CAM**   **$20.00**
Parker Brothers, 1949
A less complicated version of Parker's Camelot. It was marketed without the war reference that Camelot had.

The cover showed everyday people playing it everywhere.

CAP-IT   **$40.00**
Selchow & Righter, 1957
Designers: Ted Key, Stan & Fran Berenstain
Players had to make suitable captions for cartoons in this game. The cartoons were drawn by designers Key (who did the Hazel cartoons in the Saturday Evening Post) and the Berenstains.

CAPER   **$20.00**
Parker Brothers, 1970

CARDINO   **$5.00**
Milton Bradley, 1970

♟ CASE OF THE ELUSIVE ASSASSIN,
     ELLERY QUEEN'S $40.00
Ideal, 1967
Designer: Sid Sackson

CATCH A CHICKEN TORIE $10.00
Hasbro, 1968

CHAOS $5.00
Lakeside, 1971
This was an Aggravation type marble game.

CHASE $20.00
Cadaco, 1966
A rabbit hunt set in the Florida Everglades.
Each hazard on the gameboard was dis-
cussed in a 40 page booklet with explana-
tions as to why they were considered
dangerous.

CHASEBACK $15.00
Milton Bradley, 1962
Designer: Reuben Klamer

CHOIR, THE $20.00
3M, 1960s
Designer: Sid Sackson

CHUTE-5 $5.00
Lowe, 1973

CLUE — THE GREAT SHERLOCK HOLMES GAME $50.00
Parker Brothers, 1949
This was the first Parker Brothers version of the now-classic game.

♟ CLUE $17.00
Parker Brothers, 1956
Later versions are valued from $5.00 to $10.00.

COUNTERPOINT $7.00
Whitman, 1960s
Designer: Eddy Goldfarb

COUP D'ETAT $25.00
Parker Brothers, 1966

CRAZY THREES $5.00
Selchow & Righter, 1948

CROSS UP $15.00
Milton Bradley, 1974
Cover pictured Lucille Ball.

DEAD PAN $10.00
Selchow & Righter, 1956
Try to drop your marbles into gulleys on the pan for the highest score.

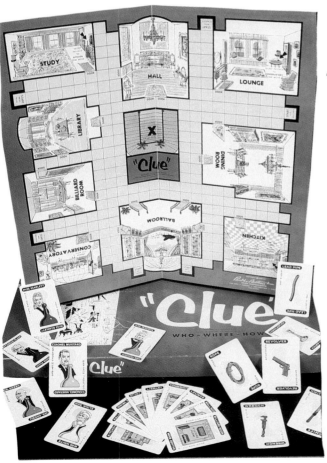

233

♟ DECOY $38.00
Selchow & Righter, 1956
This game about duck hunting came with 40 small plastic ducks and decoys. The board pictured a lake with duck blinds all around it. There is also a wooden version of this game that is valued at $65.00.

DEDUCTION $15.00
Ideal, 1976

DOLLAR BILL POKER $6.00
Lowe, 1974
TV's Odd Couple, Jack Klugman and Tony Randall graced the cover.

DOUBLE DEALER $15.00
Hasbro, 1973
Cover showed Jerry Lewis.

DUNGEON DICE $5.00
Parker Brothers, 1977

DUNGEONS & DRAGONS $20.00
TSR, 1974

♟ EDDIE CANTOR'S TELL IT
   TO THE JUDGE $25.00
Parker Brothers, 1959
Earlier versions of the radio star's game came with a small implement box and a separate board pictured here. Those are valued at $38.00.

ELECTRIC COMMIN' ROUND
   THE MOUNTAIN $40.00
Electric Game Co., 1954
Designer: Jim Prentice
Artwork: Paul Webb

ELECTRIC WHIZ CHECKERS $15.00
Electric Game Co., 1961
Designer: Jim Prentice

ELECTRIC WHIZ FARM
   ROUNDUP $20.00
Electric Game Co., 1961
Designer: Jim Prentice

ENEMY AGENT $18.00
Milton Bradley, 1976

ESCAPE FROM THE
   CASBAH $7.00
Selchow & Righter, 1975

♟ ESPIONAGE $45.00
Transogram, 1963

♟ FASCINATION CHECKERS $20.00
Remco, 1962
This version allowed no diagonal moves, only up and down, and side to side.

(Pictured on next page.)

♟ FBI $45.00
Transogram, 1961
This was based on Random House's Landmark
Book series, not the TV show.

FBI CRIME RESISTANCE GAME $10.00
Milton Bradley, 1976

FINDERS KEEPERS $8.00
Milton Bradley, 1968
Designer: Marvin Glass & Assoc.

FLINCH $4.00
Parker Brothers, 1954

♟ FLIP FLOP GO $12.00
Mattel, 1962
Players tried to trap each others flip-discs on a board
that had built-in scoring wheels.

FLIP IT 7-11 $40.00
Aurora, 1973

FLIP IT TWENTY-ONE $30.00
Aurora, 1973

FORESIGHT $15.00
Milton Bradley, 1962

FOX AND HOUNDS $20.00
Parker Brothers, 1948

♟ FU MANCHU'S HIDDEN HOARD $40.00
Ideal, 1967
Designer: Julie Cooper

GAMES GALORE! $8.00
Selchow & Righter, 1953
A compendium of six games including Hopscotch and
Horse Racing.

GINASTA $10.00
Kohner, 1954

GO $12.00
Lowe, 1951

235

GO GIN CARD GAME $10.00
Ideal, 1968

GOOD GUYS 'N BAD GUYS $10.00
Cadaco, 1973

GOOSES WILD $8.00
Co-5, 1966

GOREN'S BRIDGE FOR JUNIORS $5.00
Milton Bradley, 1959

GREAT ESTATE, THE $15.00
Hasbro, 1973
Cover showed Jerry Lewis.

♟ HARPOON $35.00
Gabriel, 1955
Here, kids could learn the subtle nuances of the lost sport of spear fishing.

♟ HEADACHE $8.00
Kohner, 1968
Came complete with the famous Pop-O-Matic that let you roll the dice with a push on a clear dome in the center of the board.

HEADS UP $3.00
Lowe, 1968
This was a "fun with numbers" dice game.

♟ HIGH GEAR $25.00
Mattel, 1962
Players became cogs in a machine where every move affected all of the players positions.

HI-Q $4.00
Kohner, 1964

HIGH BID $10.00
3M, 1965

HIGH DICE $35.00
Bettye B., 1956

HIGH STAKES $15.00
Hasbro, 1973
Cover showed Jerry Lewis.

HOLLYWOOD GO $20.00
Parker Brothers, 1954

HOODOO $12.00
Tryne Sales, 1950s

HOT SPOT! THE 1-2-3 GAME $16.00
Parker Brothers, 1961

HUNCH $10.00
Happy Hour, 1956

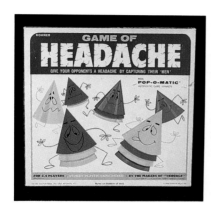

♟ INTRIGUE $32.00
Milton Bradley, 1955
Designer: Julie Cooper
This whodunit set on an ocean liner was supposed to become the Alfred Hitchcock game. However when an agreement couldn't be reached between Cooper and Bradley, the company went ahead with a different game for the Hitchcock tie-in called "Why?."

JIMMY THE GREEK ODDSMAKER POKER DICE $10.00
Aurora, 1974

JUBILEE $15.00
Cadaco, 1954

JUMPIN $10.00
3M, 1964

KARATE $8.00
Selchow & Righter, 1964
Moves were controlled by the draw and play of a special deck of cards.

KIMBO $12.00
Parker Brothers, 1960

KISMET $5.00
Lakeside, 1971

LIAR'S POKER $5.00
Transogram, 1968
This was released under the TAG (Transogram Adult Games) logo.

♟ LIE DETECTOR $45.00
Mattel, 1960
This classic game was re-released in 1965 with new suspect cards that used photographs instead of drawings.

LION HUNT $23.00
Gabriel, 1956

♟ LOST GOLD $15.00
Parker Brothers, 1975

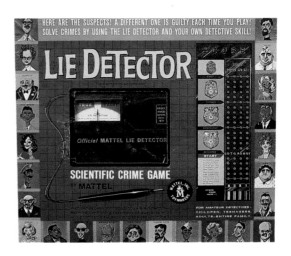

♟ MAD MAGAZINE GAME $10.00
Parker Brothers, 1979

♟ MAD MAGAZINE CARD GAME $10.00
Parker Brothers, 1980

MAGNIFICENT RACE $6.00
Parker Brothers, 1975

MAMMOTH HUNT $40.00
Cadaco, 1962
Trap prehistoric wooly mammoths.

♟ MANHUNT $18.00
Milton Bradley, 1972
Designer: Jim Houlihan
A clue scanner and battery-powered computer were
used to catch a crook in this elaborate game.

MASTERMIND $8.00
Invicta, 1972

MIKADO, GAME OF GO $10.00
Lowe, 1951

MILL GAME $11.00
Schaper, 1954

MILLE BORNES $5.00
Parker Brothers, 1962
Designer: Edmond Dujardin
A printer of sheet music and road maps, Edmond
Dujardin invented this game in 1953 which translates to
1,000 miles. Its correct pronunciation is "Meel Born."

♟ MIND MAZE $10.00
Parker Brothers, 1970
Designer: Marvin Glass & Assoc.
Set up barriers on your side of an upright board creating a maze and try to get through your opponents maze
from the reverse side using a magnet, steel ball, and
your memory.

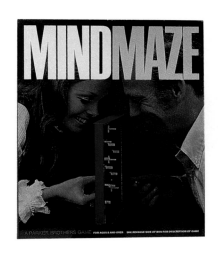

MR. REE $35.00
Selchow & Righter, 1946
Artwork: William Longyear
The game that asked the question
"Who killed Aunt Cora?" There were
many varieties of this game. The
rarest version contained plaster
heads of the suspects and is valued
at $65.00.

MYSTERY CHECKERS $10.00
Creative Ideas, 1950s

NEVER SAY DIE $6.00
Phillips, 1959
This was a lettered-dice game.

NILE $9.00
Lowe, 1967
Lowe claimed this ancient game of
strategy was "as old as the pyramids."

NIRTZ $10.00
Ideal, 1961
Designer: Reuben Klamer
Vaguely resembling Checkers, this
game gave players numbered tokens
that they had to manipulate into a
straight line across the board.

NOGGIN $7.00
Tru-Craft, 1955

ONE ARM BANDIT $8.00
Cadaco, 1966

OP TILE $6.00
Schaper, 1970s

PA-CHIZ-SI $6.00
Transogram, 1966

PARCHEESI $5.00
Selchow & Righter, 1950
S&R's bread and butter. It held the
company together and was their
biggest seller until Scrabble in the
early 1950s.

PAROLLETTE $5.00
Selchow & Righter, 1948

♟ PATHFINDER $12.00
Milton Bradley, 1970s
Designer: Jim O'Connor

PEGITY $16.00
Parker Brothers, 1953

PIRATE'S GOLD $60.00
All-Fair, 1946

PIRATE'S ISLAND $80
Corey, 1942

♟ PIT $4.00
Parker Brothers, 1973

PIVOT $6.00
Milton Bradley, 1960
Designer: Ted Starcewski

PLOTZ! $15.00
Parker Brothers, 1971

PLOY $10.00
3M, 1960s
Designer: Frank Thibault

♟ PO-KE-NO $5.00
Bee & Bicycle, 1970s

POKA-TILE $12.00
Ideal, 1961
Object was to build a regulation
poker hand around tiles already
placed on the game board.

POLLYANNA $10.00
Parker Brothers, 1950s

♟ POOCH $23.00
Hasbro, 1954

PROBE $4.00
Parker Brothers, 1964
Designer: Hank Spinnis
Guess hidden words as they are revealed one letter at a time.

PROJECT CIA $10.00
House Of Games, 1973

♟ PUT AND TAKE $5.00
Schaper, 1965

QUBIC $7.00
Parker Brothers, 1965

QUINTO $10.00
3M, 1964

♟ RACK-O $5.00
Milton Bradley, 1961
Designers: Frank Whitehead, Jim O'Connor

RANSOM $20.00
Ideal, 1961
Designer: Reuben Klamer
Each of the four players tried to capture their opponent's men and hold them for ransom.

RIO, GAME OF $30.00
Parker Brothers, 1956

♟ ROBIN HOOD $45.00
Harett-Gilmar, 1955

ROBIN HOOD $40.00
National Games, 1956

ROL-IT $7.00
Parker Brothers, 1954
Crossword game where letter cubes were rolled like dice.

ROOK $5.00
Parker Brothers, 1960
Designer: George S. Parker
Rook was designed for the South and Bible Belt where card games were discouraged by the Baptist church. It secretly became known as "Baptist Poker."

RUSSIAN ROULETTE $10.00
Selchow & Righter, 1976
In this game, you could bet your life and only lose your money.

☖ SAFARI $28.00
Selchow & Righter, 1950
Unique in that it was one of the few games that
strayed from S&R's non-violent theme policy by showing a semi-violent scene on the box. This was a jungle
adventure where bringing home big game could mean
big bucks.

SCAN $10.00
Parker Brothers, 1970

SHIFTY CHECKERS $16.00
Aurora, 1973

SHIFTY GEAR $15.00
Schaper, 1962

SINKING OF THE TITANIC $33.00
Ideal, 1976

SITUATION 4 $15.00
Parker Brothers, 1968
Designer: Marvin Glass & Assoc.

SITUATION 7 $15.00
Parker Brothers, 1969
Designer: Marvin Glass & Assoc.
I guess this game was three better than Situation 4.

SKATTERBUG $35.00
Parker Brothers, 1951

☖ SCORE FOUR $5.00
  Lakeside, 1975

☖ SEVEN-UP GAME $12.00
  Transogram, 1961
  Object was to top the most posts with your playing
  pieces.

☖ SHA-EE, GAME OF DESTINY $30.00
  Ideal, 1963
  Artwork: Ralph Pereida

SHERLOCK HOLMES'
    MURDER ON THE ORIENT EXPRESS $40.00
Ideal, 1967
Designer: Julie Cooper

SKEETER $9.00
Arco Playing Card, 1950s

SKUNK $15.00
Schaper, 1953

SLEUTH $15.00
3M, 1971
Designer: Sid Sackson

SLIP DISC $15.00
Mattel, 1971
Designers: Alan Hill, Derek Gay
Pull the spring-action pegs on both sides of the playing box to guess which rods hold your opponent's disc.

SMESS $8.00
Parker Brothers, 1970
Designer: Reuben Klamer
Artwork: Jack McMann
This strategy game was also a spoof of chess.

SNAFU $10.00
Haswell, 1952

♟ SNAKE EYES $55.00
Selchow & Righter, 1940s
The catalog states "Women like the game cause it's easy, men chuckle because of the humorous cards." Believe it or not, this cover appeared on store shelves until 1957. Versions after 1957 are valued at $25.00.

SNAPSHOT $8.00
Parker Brothers, 1972
Designer: Marvin Glass & Assoc.

♟ SOLOTAIRE $6.00
Milton Bradley, 1973
Cover pictures Lucille Ball.

♟ SORRY $10.00
Parker Brothers, 1954

SPLAT $15.00
Mattel, 1968

♟ SPY DETECTOR $35.00
Mattel, 1963
The familiar faces of Mattel's 1960 Lie Detector were back with updated looks and new occupations in this game. It was also released as Agent ZERO M Spy Detector in conjunction with Mattel's line of secret agent toys.

SQUARE-IT $25.00
Hasbro, 1961

SQUARES $12.00
Schaper, 1954

SQUARESVILLE $6.00
Cadaco, 1968
Plastic gameboard held sticks and markers that you strategically placed to complete as many squares as possible while keeping your opponent from doing the same.

STADIUM CHECKERS $10.00
Schaper, 1952

STAY ALIVE $10.00
Milton Bradley, 1971
Designer: Marvin Glass & Assoc.
Pull levers to send opponent's marbles down the holes. Be the sole survivor — the last player with marbles on the elevated plastic board — to win.

STRATEGY POKER $7.00
Milton Bradley, 1967

STUMP $10.00
Milton Bradley, 1968

♟ SUPER SPY $25.00
Milton Bradley, 1971
Designer: Jim Houlihan
Prowl from room to room inside enemy headquarters picking up documents while avoiding a metal disc underneath the board that would set off an alarm and set you back.

♟ SWAHILI $17.00
Milton Bradley, 1968

TAKE 12 $7.00
Phillips, 1959

TANGLE $5.00
Selchow & Righter, 1964
Block, surround, and capture hexagons with varied-shaped pieces.

TEE'D OFF $15.00
Milton Bradley, 1966
This was a race against time to see who could jump and remove the most golf tees from a triangle board. It's similar to the games you find on the tables at better roadside diners.

THE OLD SHELL GAME $5.00
Selchow & Righter, 1974
Object was to make your opponents guess which plastic walnut shells concealed the peas.

THIMK $15.00
Hasbro, 1964

THIMK $10.00
Tryne Sales, 1955

THIRTEEN $9.00
Cadaco, 1959

THISTLE $10.00
Parker Brothers, 1966

THREE MUSKETEERS $30.00
Milton Bradley, 1950

TIC TAC TOWER $6.00
Selchow & Righter, 1969
A three-dimensional version of tic-tac-toe.

TOP COP $65.00

Cadaco, 1961

Junior G-Men would search for clues to capture robbers on the "Wanted" list. The first to get three was the Top Cop.

♟ TOP ME $13.00

Standard Toykraft, 1957

TOP SECRET $65.00

National Games, 1956

TOPPER $14.00

Lakeside, 1962

♟ TRACK AND TRAP $16.00

Whitman, 1969

TRAP $15.00

Ideal, 1972

Designers: Eddy & Anita Goldfarb

♟ TRAPPED!, ELLERY QUEEN'S GREAT
    MYSTERY GAME $50.00

Bettye B., 1956

TRAP 'EM $28.00

Selchow & Righter, 1957

This was similar to S & R's game, Safari, where you decide to either trap or shoot animals depending on their relative value to zoos.

♟ TRAP THE RAT $14.00

Hasbro, 1964

My, this one sounds very similar to a hit game released the year before — Mouse Trap.

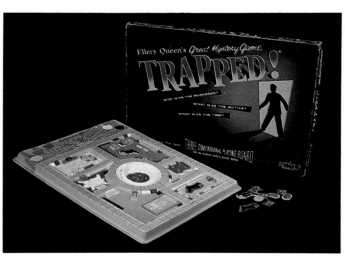

TREASURE ISLAND $45.00
American, 1954

TREASURE ISLAND $55.00
Harett-Gilmar, 1955

TRIPOLY $7.00
Cadaco, 1968

♟ TROKE $7.00
Selchow & Righter, 1962
Another game that combined
the speed of checkers and the
skill and strategy of chess.

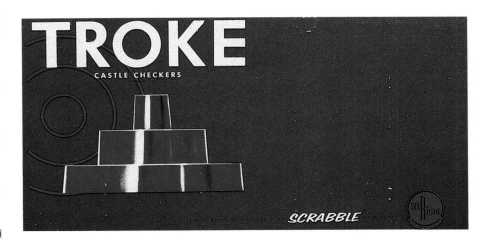

♟ TROUBLE $8.00
Kohner, 1965
This variant of Parcheesi came complete with
the famous Pop-O-Matic that let you roll the
dice with a push on a clear dome in the center of
the board.

TWIXT $15.00
3M, 1962
Designers: Bill Carrison, Alex Randolph

WA-HOO $16.00
Creative Designs, 1950s

WAHOO $25.00
Zondine, 1947

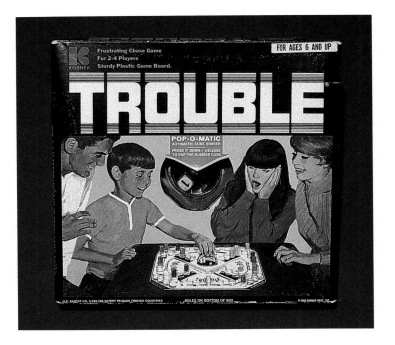

♟ WATERWORKS $5.00
Parker Brothers, 1972
Artwork: Jack McMann

WHO? $30.00
Parker Brothers, 1951

WHODUNIT $14.00
Hasbro, 1968

WHODUNIT $9.00
Selchow & Righter, 1973

INDEX

ABOUT THE AUTHOR

Rick Polizzi is co-author of the widely-acclaimed coffee table book *Spin Again: Board Games from the Fifties and Sixties* (Chronicle Books), and publisher and editor of its off-shoot publication, *Spin Again* — a quarterly magazine available throughout North America and Europe. Rick, a graduate of the American Academy of Dramatic Arts, has done many character voices for animated TV shows and is currently a screenwriter in Los Angeles where he lives with his wife, Carla, and their daughter, Hannah.

Schroeder's
ANTIQUES
Price Guide

. . . is the #1 best-selling antiques & collectibles value guide on the market today, and here's why . . .

Schroeder's ANTIQUES Price Guide

OUR #1 BEST SELLER!

Identification & Values Of Over 50,000 Antiques & Collectibles

8½ x 11, 608 Pages, $14.95

- *More than 300 advisors, well-known dealers, and top-notch collectors work together with our editors to bring you accurate information regarding pricing and identification.*

- *More than 45,000 items in almost 500 categories are listed along with hundreds of sharp original photos that illustrate not only the rare and unusual, but the common, popular collectibles as well.*

- *Each large close-up shot shows important details clearly. Every subject is represented with histories and background information, a feature not found in any of our competitors' publications.*

- *Our editors keep abreast of newly developing trends, often adding several new categories a year as the need arises.*

If it merits the interest of today's collector, you'll find it in *Schroeder's*. And you can feel confident that the information we publish is up to date and accurate. Our advisors thoroughly check each category to spot inconsistencies, listings that may not be entirely reflective of market dealings, and lines too vague to be of merit. Only the best of the lot remains for publication.

Without doubt, you'll find
SCHROEDER'S ANTIQUES PRICE GUIDE
the only one to buy for
reliable information and values.

COLLECTOR BOOKS
A Division of Schroeder Publishing Co., Inc.